1/12/6

Supplement to Smith's

MARINE ALGAE OF THE
MONTEREY PENINSULA

Supplement to Smith's

MARINE ALGAE OF THE
MONTEREY PENINSULA

George J. Hollenberg
and
Isabella A. Abbott

STANFORD UNIVERSITY PRESS
Stanford, California
1966

Stanford University Press
Stanford, California
© 1966 by the Board of Trustees of the
Leland Stanford Junior University
Printed in the United States of America
.L.C. 66-18757

Dedicated in Admiration and Affection
to the Memory of
Gilbert Morgan Smith

PREFACE

More than twenty years have elapsed since the publication by Gilbert Morgan Smith of *Marine Algae of the Monterey Peninsula, California*. The book has gained the respect and affection of many hundreds of biologists, teachers, students, and beachcombers, and has gone through three printings since publication by Stanford University Press in 1944.

Marine Algae is remarkable both for the sustained excellence of Dr. Smith's work and for the great breadth of the flora described. In his Preface, Dr. Smith observed that "the [algal] flora of the Monterey Peninsula is far richer than that of any other portion of the west coast of this country." The flora would seem now to be richer even than Dr. Smith had imagined it: during these twenty-two years, some 55 species of algae have been added to the Monterey flora, a surprisingly large number for an area so well studied. The development of improved equipment for underwater diving has made possible vertical extensions of the distribution records, as well. Moreover, knowledge of structure, physiology, and reproduction has been advanced considerably by laboratory study of hundreds of species.

The effect of the information thus amassed, however, has been not so much an invalidation of Smith's work as an enlargement upon it. The purpose of this *Supplement*, then, is to bring the information in Smith up to date without materially revising his book. We have therefore adhered scrupulously to the format and general taxonomic sequence of the Smith, and reserve for another time such revisions as would have no important bearing on the essential content and usefulness of the book.

Toward that end, the descriptions in the *Supplement* include nothing that is already in the Smith, and are heavily cross-referenced to corresponding discussions in Smith. The details of presentation and cross-referencing are explained in the Introduction.

vii

A bibliography and an index have been prepared for the new material in the *Supplement*; these are also discussed in the Introduction. The index is arranged to facilitate cross-referencing to the Smith.

The descriptions in the *Supplement* are shared jointly by the authors, although the senior author was responsible for all of the green algae and most of the brown algae, and the junior author for most of the red algae and all of the keys.

A work of this kind, small in comparison to the prodigious work of Dr. Smith, can be achieved only with the cooperation of various colleagues and herbaria. We wish to express our great appreciation for loans of herbarium materials to the Curators of the Herbaria of the University of British Columbia (Dr. Robert F. Scagel); the University of Washington (Dr. Richard E. Norris); the University of California, Berkeley (Dr. George F. Papenfuss and Dr. Paul C. Silva); the Dudley Herbarium of Stanford University (Dr. Richard Holm); the University of California, Santa Barbara (Dr. Michael Neushul); the Beaudette Foundation (Dr. E. Yale Dawson); and the Allan Hancock Foundation (Dr. E. Yale Dawson and Dr. John Garth). We also gratefully acknowledge loans from Dr. Maxwell S. Doty, University of Hawaii; the Botanical Museum, Lund University, Sweden; and the Farlow Herbarium of Harvard University. The junior author is greatly indebted to Professor Yukio Yamada, Faculty of Science, Hokkaido University, for the use of facilities and the opportunity to work with a superior collection of algae, and to the U.S.–Japan Cooperative Science Program for making this possible.

Many new specimens have been added to the Gilbert M. Smith Herbarium at Hopkins Marine Station by our students, particularly Lester E. Hair, William C. Austin, James McLean, and Hayden R. Williams. Their interest and cooperation have been a stimulus to our studies. To our colleague Dr. Wheeler J. North, of the California Institute of Technology, we are indebted for the outstanding collections of subtidal algae he has given us. No other group of collections has furnished us with more new records or new species than has his.

A special note of appreciation is due to Miss Dana Bean, whose illustrations are a lively translation of our observations.

We are also pleased to acknowledge the support and encouragement of the directors of the Hopkins Marine Station: Professor-Emeritus Lawrence R. Blinks and Associate Professor John H. Phillips.

GEORGE J. HOLLENBERG

ISABELLA A. ABBOTT

January 1966

CONTENTS

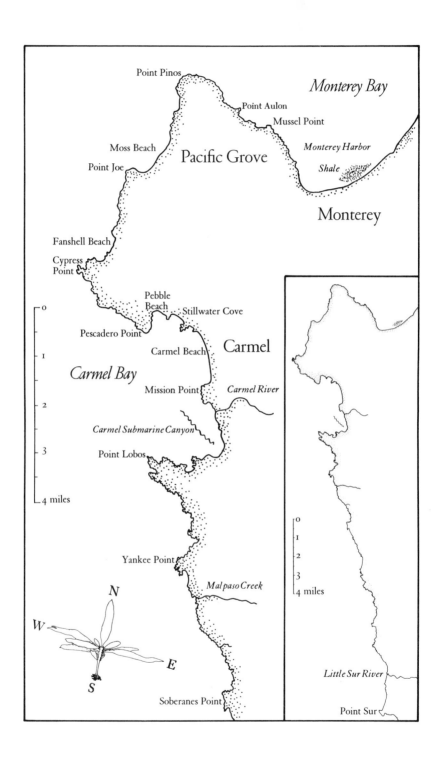

Point Pinos

Monterey Bay

Point Aulon

Mussel Point

Moss Beach

Pacific Grove

Monterey Harbor

Shale

Point Joe

Monterey

Fanshell Beach

Cypress
Point

Pebble
Beach

Stillwater Cove

Pescadero Point

Carmel Beach

Carmel

0

Carmel Bay

Mission Point

Carmel River

1

2

Carmel Submarine Canyon

3

Point Lobos

4 miles

Yankee Point

Malpaso Creek

N

0
1
2
3
4 miles

W

E

S

Little Sur River

Soberanes Point

Point Sur

Supplement to Smith's

MARINE ALGAE OF THE
MONTEREY PENINSULA

INTRODUCTION

Our rationale in assembling this *Supplement* has been, first, to collect and evaluate all recorded and suggested additions and revisions to the Smith; second, to weed out of the valid data thus assembled the tentative, the trivial, the peripheral, and the largely esoteric; third, to repeat nothing that is as valid in 1966 as it was in 1944; and fourth, to tie everything to its corresponding discussion in Smith.

Thus we have emulated the style, treatment, methods of citation, and even the typography of the Smith, so that there might be complete continuity in the use of the two books. Further, we have included in the *Supplement* Bibliography only those references not referred to by Smith; the Index has been designed to reflect, at a glance, the nature of each entry's relationship to the Smith; and we have employed a system of margin references (explained below) relating every taxon in the *Supplement* to its corresponding discussion in the Smith. Moreover, certain elements of the Smith—Preface, Introduction, Location Names, Glossary, and Bibliography — should be considered integral parts of the *Supplement,* as well.

We have made two small departures from this plan. We have taken the liberty of including more of the coastline of Monterey County in the range of interest—beyond, and especially to the south, of the Monterey Peninsula itself. And we have neither added to nor changed the very useful "Keys to the Genera of Marine Algae" of Smith (pp. 399–412). We believe that these keys, constructed from nontechnical characters and used by Dr. Smith's students for perhaps 15 years before their appearance in *Marine Algae* in 1944, should be revised only after we have had more experience accommodating the newcomers to this flora.

The emphasis in the *Supplement* is upon describing genera and species new to the Monterey algal flora, and on noting changes in nomenclature that reflect the present-day understanding of the various species. In the orders, families, and genera where important changes or new additions have been made, revised keys are included, and, where necessary, revised descriptions also.

Each of the 259 entries in the *Supplement* is included for one of four reasons, and is so identified by a distinct symbol placed in the margin. Each of these margin symbols is followed immediately by numerals indicating the page number of related discussion in Smith. The four categories of information are also distinguished typographically in the Index, in the manner of the Smith Index.

New additions ("NA" in the margins, 55 species, 19 genera, one family) represent new records for the marine algal flora of the Monterey area, and are presented in the same full manner as the entries in Smith. These have been described or recorded elsewhere by ourselves or by others, since publication of the Smith, or, where marked with an asterisk (below and in the Index), are recorded from this area for the first time. New additions are distinguished in the Index by boldface type. The *Supplement* describes the following species new to this area:

Ulothrix pseudoflacca
Monostroma oxyspermum
Monostroma grevillei
Bryopsis pennatula
Ectocarpus confervoides
　　　v. *parvus*
Desmarestia tabacoides
　Phaeostrophion irregulare
　Coilodesme plana
Pelagophycus porra
Eisenia arborea
Fucus distichus
　　　subsp. *edentatus* f. *abbreviatus*
　Pelvetiopsis arborescens
Conchocelis rosea
Acrochaetium amphiroae
Acrochaetium microscopicum
Acrochaetium desmarestiae
Gelidium setchellii
Gloiopeltis furcata
　Peyssonelia profunda
　Rhodophysema minus

Lithothamnion aculeiferum
Lithothamnion phymatodeum
Lithophyllum decipiens
Lithophyllum imitans
Yamadaea melobesioides
　Serraticardia macmillani
Calliarthron schmittii
　Calliarthron tuberculosum
Cryptonemia borealis
Cryptonemia obovata
　Halymenia schizymenioides
Dermocorynus occidentalis
　Kallymenia norrisii
　Callophyllis thompsonii
　Callophyllis heanophylla
　Pugetia fragilissima
Sarcodiotheca furcata
Gracilaria verrucosa
Petroglossum parvum
Fauchea fryeana
Fauchea galapagensis
Fryeella gardneri

Maripelta rotata
Rhodymenia callophyllidoides
*Rhodymeniocolax botryoidea
Callithamnion lejolisea
*Holmesia californica
Nitophyllum northii
*Acrosorium uncinatum

*Botryoglossum ruprechtiana
*Heterosiphonia asymmetria
*Veloroa subulata
*Pterosiphonia gracilis
Laurencia blinksii
*Laurencia subopposita

Name changes ("NC" in the margins, 75 species, 20 genera, eight families, one order, and two subclasses) represent species (or other taxa) recorded in Smith whose names have been changed for reasons of nomenclature. A species may have its name changed but remain in the same genus; or it may have its name changed and be transferred to another genus, or even to another family or order. Literature references pertinent to each name change are listed, and in many cases the reasons for the change are explicitly given; where no literature references appear, the change is made herein, by the authors, and has not been previously recorded. Where similar changes have occurred with genera, families, or orders, the treatment is much the same. All name-change entries include the attendant synonymy details. Many name-change entries also include new information, as defined below, but are not so identified in the margins.

A special comment may be useful concerning several of the name changes: one species (*Erythrophyllum delesserioides*) has been transferred to another order with no change in status; two species (*Codiolum petrocelidis* and *Gracilaria linearis*) have undergone certain changes in the process of being transferred to other orders; and seven genera and species (*Codiolum, Colpomenia sinuosa, Dictyota flabellata, Porphyra variegata, Lobocolax, Iridaea sanguinea,* and *Taenioma*) have been removed from the Monterey flora—but have not in the process been necessarily invalidated elsewhere.

In the Index, all species names or other taxon names (other than new additions) that occur in the *Supplement* but do not in Smith are distinguished by capital and small-capital letters; those marked with a double dagger (‡) are new combinations or uses of names for species already in this flora, but used here for the first time. The Index also provides a useful cross-reference to the synonymies (former plant names) that are cited in the nomenclatural explanations in the *Supplement*; these are distinguished in the Index by italic type. Those plant names recognized by Smith that have since become synonymies—via name change, transfer, or whatever—are further distinguished in the Index by a dagger (†).

Revisions have occasionally been made in the basic descriptions of species or other taxa, and in the keys to species (genera, etc.) in the local flora, and are so designated by an "R" in the margin. Where an entry includes both a name change and a revision of some sort, the margin symbol "NC,R" is used. Many entries labeled R or NC,R also include new information, as defined below, but are not so identified. In the Index, entries in the revisions category are set in plain roman type, and are further distinguished by letters following the entries ("RD" for revised description, "RK" for revised key, "RDK" for revised description and key). "NC,R" entries appear in the Index in capital and small-capital letters followed by "RD," "RK," or "RDK." The *Supplement* contains revised descriptions for 18 species, 23 genera, nine families, and four orders, and revised keys for 28 genera, 22 families, six orders, and two subclasses. It should also be noted, in the text, that the page-number references given in the keys are to the Smith, not the *Supplement*.

All remaining entries in the *Supplement* comprise the category *new information,* or "NI." These are entries that embrace no name change or descriptive revision, but that provide information of other sorts, such as new local distribution records, new information on reproductive history, or short notes of similar miscellaneous nature. In this category, for example, is information on the habitat of species previously known only from specimens cast ashore. New-information entries in the Index, like revision entries, are set in plain roman type, but are followed by "NI." There are new-information entries for 18 species, three genera, three families, and one order. As we have mentioned, many *Supplement* entries in the name-change or revision categories include new information as well, but are not so identified in the margins or in the Index.

The addition of a new species to a genus may require that the description or the key for the genus be revised, but will probably have no effect on the family or order to which the genus belongs. Where this is the case, the family or order involved is simply named, as a roadmarking convenience to the reader, and is included in the Index, in plain roman type.

Finally, it might be mentioned that 53 new illustrations have been prepared for the *Supplement,* and that the figure numbers appearing immediately below the Smith page-number references in the margins refer to these illustrations.

DIVISION CHLOROPHYTA

Class CHLOROPHYCEAE 25

Order ULOTRICHALES 32

Family ULOTRICHACEAE 33

Ulothrix pseudoflacca Wille   NA33

Wille, 1901, p. 22; pl. 2, figs. 64–81.

Filaments, as found on the Monterey Peninsula, 1–4 mm. long, 22–25 μ broad, composed of cells 0.3–1.0 diameters long. Cell walls thin, the chloroplast encircling the cell, with a single pyrenoid. Filaments attached by an elongate cell narrowed toward the base. Fertile cells not enlarged.

LOCAL DISTRIBUTION. Attached to a boat bottom, Pacific Grove.

TYPE LOCALITY. On rocks at the Biological Station, Dröbak, near Oslo, Norway.

PACIFIC COAST DISTRIBUTION. Alaska (Sitka) to central California (Pacific Grove).

Differing from *U. implexa* in having cells much shorter than broad.   34

Order ULVALES   NI41

This order was created for those genera of blade-like algae that show an alternation of isomorphic generations. Since the publication of Smith's book in 1944, many workers have shown that *Monostroma* contains some species that exhibit an alternation of heteromorphic generations, and have removed that genus from this order on that account. Since the life histories of the local species of *Monostroma* have not been extensively studied, we continue to include these species in the Order Ulvales.

KEY TO THE FAMILIES IN THE LOCAL FLORA   R42

1. Adult thallus wholly or in part tubular and monostromatic; or blade-like and distromatic.................Ulvaceae (p. 42; below)
1. Adult thallus an expanded blade, monostromatic throughout............................Monostromaceae (below)

R42

Family ULVACEAE

Thalli tubular, the tubes only 1 cell thick, with or without a prostrate base, or thalli expanded into broad blades two cells thick. Life cycle with isomorphic generations. (See also Smith's remarks on Order Ulvales.)

R42

REVISED KEY TO THE GENERA IN THE LOCAL FLORA

1. Adult thallus wholly or in part tubular, monostromatic.............. 2
1. Adult thallus a broadly expanded blade, distromatic........*Ulva* (p. 43)
    2. Tubes arising from prostrate, disc-like base.......*Blidingia* (below)
    2. Tubes without a prostrate base, the basal tubular portions
        with internal rhizoids...................*Enteromorpha* (p. 48)

NC,R50

Blidingia Kylin, 1947

Thallus clearly of two parts: a prostrate, discoid base; and, arising from the base, one or more erect tubes, with walls of each tube composed of a single layer of cells with a thick outer membrane.

Plants of this genus differ from *Enteromorpha* in possessing the discoid base. Furthermore, no gametes have ever been observed in plants of this genus, whereas they are known in many species of *Enteromorpha*.

STRUCTURE AND REPRODUCTION. Kylin, 1947, pp. 1–9.

With one species in the local flora.

NC50
FIG. 1

Blidingia minima (Nägeli) Kylin var. *minima* Kylin

Kylin, 1947, p. 8.

Enteromorpha minima Nägeli *in* Kützing, 1849, p. 482. Collins, 1903, p. 24; pl. 42, figs. 9–10. Setchell and Gardner, 1920, p. 250. Smith, 1944, p. 50; pl. 5, fig. 8. We exclude from synonymy Doty's (1947, p. 17) and Scagel's (1957, p. 37) interpretations of Smith's *Enteromorpha micrococca*.

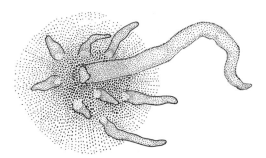

FIG. 1.—*Blidingia minima*. Habit of plant, showing erect portion arising from a prostrate disc. ×1

The information concerning the discoid base should be added to Smith's description. His illustration (pl. 5, fig. 8) should show the discoid base, as we have shown in the accompanying figure.

Family MONOSTROMACEAE   NC,R42

Thalli expanded into blades, monostromatic throughout. Life cycle with heteromorphic generations, the large leafy thallus representing the sporophyte, and a disc-shaped thallus the gametophyte (in *M. zostericola* from Japan).

With one genus, *Monostroma,* in the local flora.

Monostroma Thuret, 1854

KEY TO THE SPECIES IN THE LOCAL FLORA   R43

1. Frond saccate 2
1. Frond an expanded sheet...................*M. oxyspermum* (below)
   2. Blades cuneate, irregularly lobed, with slender stipes; cells
      rectangular to vertical-elongate in section....*M. zostericola* (p. 43)
   2. Blades usually retaining sac-like habit and irregularly shaped
      after splitting; cells horizontally oval in section *M. grevillei* (below)

Monostroma oxyspermum (Kützing) Doty   NA43

Doty, 1947, p. 12 (including synonymy).
Ulva oxysperma Kützing, 1843, p. 296.

Thalli, as found on the Monterey Peninsula, 1–2 cm. broad, of orbicular shape, mostly as long as broad; pale grass-green. Cells quadrate, with 1 pyrenoid per cell; membrane 15–16 µ thick.

LOCAL DISTRIBUTION. Collected from a small jetty, Monterey Harbor; and from ditches and marshes at the mouth of Carmel River.

TYPE LOCALITY. "Ostsee; Schleybusen bei Winning."

PACIFIC COAST DISTRIBUTION. Southern British Columbia to southern California.

Monostroma grevillei (Thuret) Wittrock   NA43

Wittrock, 1866, p. 57; pl. 4, fig. 14. Collins, 1909, p. 209. Setchell and Gardner, 1903, p. 208. Setchell and Gardner, 1920, p. 236.
Enteromorpha grevillei Thuret, 1854*A*, p. 25.

Thalli, as found on the Monterey Peninsula, at first oval and saccate, up to 3 cm. high and 2 cm. broad, later splitting to form a number of divisions, yellowish-green in color. Membrane delicate, 21–30 µ thick, with cells compact and angular, 9–15 µ in diameter and generally longer in the cross section of the membrane, and with a single chromatophore and 1–3 pyrenoids per cell. Gametes (?) biflagellate, 3 by 7 µ.

LOCAL DISTRIBUTION. Epiphytic on *Phyllospadix* and on *Leptocladia,* Middle Reef of Moss Beach.

TYPE LOCALITY. Atlantic shores of Europe.

PACIFIC COAST DISTRIBUTION. Alaska to central California, but as noted by Setchell and Gardner, essentially limited to the northern portion of the range.

52

Order SCHIZOGONIALES

NI52

FAMILY SCHIZOGONIACEAE

With one genus, *Prasiola,* in the local flora. For *Rosenvingiella* (= *Gayella*), see comment following *Prasiola meridionalis.*

R53

Prasiola Meneghini, 1838

Thalli of two types. One, the *Prasiola* stage, is formed of small, monostromatic, slightly expanded blades 4–11 mm. tall, with curled edges, attached by filamentous outgrowths of the margin or base. Cells cubical to rectangular or rounded, at times appearing in groups, the groups in a linear series giving the thallus a grid-like appearance. Cells uninucleate with a single large, stellate chloroplast, with one pyrenoid. The other, or *Rosenvingiella* stage, with thallus filamentous, of one to several cells in width; structure of the cells similar to that of *Prasiola.*

Thalli multiplying vegetatively by fragmentation, producing the *Rosenvingiella* stage, or asexually by large spores giving rise to the *Rosenvingiella* stage or the *Prasiola* stage.

Sexual reproduction oögamous by biflagellate microgametes and by large macrogametes, formed in special cells of the thallus.

STRUCTURE AND REPRODUCTION. Friedmann, 1959, pp. 571–94. Bravo, 1962, pp. 17–23; 1965, pp. 177–94.

With one species in the local flora.

NC53,54 **Prasiola meridionalis** Setchell and Gardner

Setchell and Gardner, 1920*A*, p. 291; pl. 25, fig. 2. Setchell and Gardner, 1920, p. 278; pl. 20, fig. 2. Smith, 1944, p. 53; pl. 2, figs. 10–15. Bravo, 1962, pp. 17–23; 1965, pp. 177–94.

Rosenvingiella constricta (Setchell and Gardner) Silva, 1957, p. 41.

Gayella constricta Setchell and Gardner *in* Gardner, 1917, p. 384; pl. 32, fig. 5; pl. 33, figs. 5–9. Setchell and Gardner, 1920, p. 280; pl. 12, figs. 5–10. Smith, 1944, p. 54; pl. 2, figs. 8–9.

Bravo's studies of the life history of this species were done on plants collected off Mussel Point. She was able to compare these plants in the field with those she grew in culture, and was able to demonstrate conclusively that *Rosenvingiella constricta* is a stage in the life history of *Prasiola meridionalis*. She also found that both stages were diploid. *Prasiola* is more common than *Rosenvingiella* during the summer and fall. Gametes are produced by both stages in winter.

Rosenvingiella Silva, 1957
(= Gayella Rosenvinge, 1893)

NC54

Silva, 1957, p. 41. Rosenvinge, 1893, p. 936. Not *Gayella* Pierre, 1890, a genus of flowering plants.

Rosenvingiella has been demonstrated to be a stage in the life history of *Prasiola* (see above). The genus may therefore be removed from the flora.

Order CLADOPHORALES

54.

Family CLADOPHORACEAE

55

Spongomorpha Kützing, 1843

NI64

Life histories of most species of *Spongomorpha* are unknown, and although it has been well demonstrated that *Codiolum petrocelidis* is a phase in the life history of the West Coast *Spongomorpha coalita,* other species of *Codiolum* in other regions have been suggested as phases in the life history of other genera. Moreover, there are many species of *Spongomorpha* in Japan, but no reports of any species of *Codiolum*.

With one species in the local flora.

Spongomorpha coalita (Ruprecht) Collins

R65

Smith, 1944, p. 64 (including synonymy).
Codiolum petrocelidis Kuckuck, 1894, p. 259. Smith, 1944, p. 68. Hollenberg, 1958, p. 249. Fan, 1959, p. 1.

Thallus of two types. That of the *Spongomorpha* stage is up to 25 cm. tall, grass-green to dark green in color. Branches with recurved branchlets holding branches together like a frayed rope. Cells multinucleate, those of lower portion broader than long, those of upper portion 3–6 times longer than broad. Thalli heterothallic, isogamous. Zygotes give rise to an independent, nearly microscopic plant heretofore known as *Codiolum petrocelidis,* which inhabits *Petrocelis* as an endophyte, but which may be free living. Thallus a unicellular, multinucleate vesicle with a prominent stalk for each vesicle. Stalk elongate, pushing the vesicle deep within the host tissue. On germination, the vesicle produces zoospores that give rise to the *Spongomorpha* stage, or the vesicle produces the *Spon-*

gomorpha stage directly (although we doubt that the direct production occurs under natural conditions).

65 ## Order CHLOROCOCCALES

NI66 ### Family ENDOSPHAERACEAE
The key to the genera may be removed; see *Codiolum,* below.

NC68 ### Codiolum Braun, 1855

Codiolum petrocelidis Kuckuck has been shown to be a stage in the life history of *Spongomorpha coalita* (see above). The genus may therefore be removed from the flora.

68 ## Order SIPHONALES

72 ### Family BRYOPSIDACEAE

Bryopsis Lamouroux, 1809

R73 REVISED KEY TO THE SPECIES IN THE LOCAL FLORA

1. Erect branches pinnately branched..............*B. corticulans* (p. 73)
1. Erect branches radially branched................................. 2
  2. The branches profuse......................*B. hypnoides* (p. 73)
  2. The branches few, sometimes lacking........*B. pennatula* (below)

NA73 ### Bryopsis pennatula J. G. Agardh

J. G. Agardh, 1847, p. 6. Kützing, 1849, p. 492. Kützing, 1856, vol. 6, p. 27; pl. 76, fig. II.
Bryopsis pennata var. *minor* J. G. Agardh, 1886, part 5, p. 23.
Bryopsis pennata Collins, 1909, p. 405 (in part) (not of Lamouroux).

Thalli, as found on the Monterey Peninsula, up to 3 cm. high, from matted basal filaments, with simple erect branches bearing relatively few short nondistichous pinnules at the tip.

LOCAL DISTRIBUTION. Growing at about the 0.0-foot tide level, Mussel Point.

TYPE LOCALITY. St. Augustin, Pacific Mexico.

PACIFIC COAST DISTRIBUTION. Central California to Mexico.

When the substratum is suitable (e.g., sponge tissue) the rhizoidal attachment may involve a penetrating branch resembling a taproot.

DIVISION PHAEOPHYTA

Family Ectocarpaceae

Ectocarpus Lyngbye, 1819   R79

Chromatophore band-shaped or plate-shaped. Otherwise, as described in Smith.

---

* Dixon and Russell (1964) have pointed out that two orthographic variants *Pylaiella* and *Pilayella* have been used, both commemorating the same person (usually referred to as De la Pylaie) who spelled his own name as Pylaie and Pilaye. *Pilayella* has the right of priority and is therefore the correct spelling to be used.

NA79
Fig. 2

Ectocarpus confervoides var. parvus (Saunders) Setchell and Gardner.

Setchell and Gardner, 1922, p. 414. Setchell and Gardner, 1925, p. 413.
Ectocarpus siliculosus var. *parvus* Saunders, 1898, p. 153; pl. 22, figs. 1–9.

Plants forming tufts or covering extensive areas, 1–2 cm. high, with frequent alternate branching. Branches tapering and often ending in a long colorless hair. Cells of main filaments 20–30 μ broad and 1–3 times as long as broad, slightly constricted at the cross walls. Chromatophores irregularly band-shaped. Plurilocular organs narrowly lanceolate to conical, 120–400 μ long and 20–27 μ wide, occasionally seriate, usually sessile.

LOCAL DISTRIBUTION. From a boat bottom at Pacific Grove; and from a mooring line in Monterey Harbor.

TYPE LOCALITY. San Pedro, California.

PACIFIC COAST DISTRIBUTION. Central California (San Francisco) to southern California (San Diego).

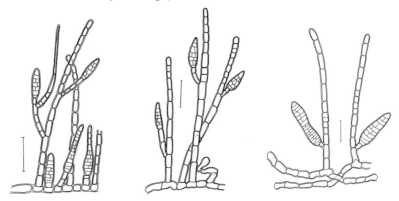

FIG. 2 (*left*)—*Ectocarpus confervoides* var. *parvus*. Habit of thallus growing on *Nereocystis*. (Rule represents 100μ.)

FIG. 3 (*center*)—*Ectocarpus confervoides* var. *pygmaeus*. Habit of plant growing on *Dictyoneurum*. (Rule represents 30μ.)

FIG. 4 (*right*)—*Feldmannia chitonicola*. Habit of thallus growing on back of *Cryptochiton*. (Rule represents 100μ.)

This variety is usually larger than var. *pygmaeus,* and differs in the length of the plurilocular organs and in having tapering erect filaments.

Ectocarpus confervoides var. pygmaeus (Areschoug) Kjellman

NI84
FIG. 3

(New illustration prepared; compare with that for var. *parvus.*)

Ectocarpus dimorphus Silva

NC85

Silva, 1957, p. 42.
Ectocarpus variabilis (Saunders) Smith, 1942, p. 657; figs. 1–4 (including synonymy). Not *E. variabilis* Vickers (1905, p. 59).

Giffordia Hamel, 1939

NC,R81–82, 89

Thalli tufted, of medium height, strongly branched, meristems toward the apex or the base. Chromatophores discoid. Plurilocular organs ovoid or obtuse, generally unequal laterally, always sessile, very often in series.

STRUCTURE AND REPRODUCTION. Hamel, 1939, pp. x–xi.

KEY TO THE SPECIES IN THE LOCAL FLORA

R81–82

1. Major branches corticated at least basally.......................... 2
1. Erect branches never corticated...........*G. saundersii* (p. 89; below)
   2. Branches abruptly constricted at
      their bases......................*G. granulosoides* (p. 82; below)
   2. Branches not constricted at their bases......................... 3
3. Thalli coarse and rigid, branches mostly opposite
    or whorled.............................*G. granulosa* (p. 81; below)
3. Thalli densely matted, branches mostly alternate
    or secund...............................*G. oviger* (p. 82; below)

Giffordia granulosa (J. E. Smith) Hamel

NC81

Basonym: *Ectocarpus granulosa* (J. E. Smith) C. A. Agardh, 1828, p. 45. Anderson, 1891, p. 219. Howe, 1893, p. 67.
Conferva granulosa J. E. Smith *in* English Botany, 1814, p. 2351; pl. 2351.
Ectocarpus granulosus (J. E. Smith) C. A. Agardh of Saunders, 1898, p. 156; pl. 24, figs. 3–5. Of Setchell and Gardner, 1925, p. 426. Of Smith, 1944, p. 81; pl. 11, figs. 1–2.
This species is the lectotype of the genus *Giffordia* (Hamel, 1939, p. 18).

Giffordia saundersii (Setchell and Gardner) Hollenberg and Abbott, new comb.

NC89

Basonym: *Ectocarpus saundersii* Setchell and Gardner, 1922D, p. 411.
Ectocarpus saundersii Setchell and Gardner, 1925, p. 434. Smith, 1944, p. 89 (including synonymy).

NC82   **Giffordia granulosoides** (Setchell and Gardner) Hollenberg and Abbott, new comb.

> Basonym: *Ectocarpus granulosoides* Setchell and Gardner, 1922D, p. 410; pl. 45, figs. 7–8.
> *Ectocarpus granulosoides* Setchell and Gardner, 1925, p. 431. Smith, 1944, p. 82; pl. 11, figs. 3–4.

NC82   **Giffordia oviger** (Harvey) Hollenberg and Abbott, new comb.

> Basonym: *Ectocarpus oviger* Harvey, 1862, p. 167.
> *Ectocarpus oviger* Harvey, Setchell and Gardner, 1925, p. 428. Smith, 1944, p. 82 (including synonymy).

NC,R87–88   <h2 style="text-align:center">Feldmannia Hamel, 1939</h2>

Thalli tufted, branching mostly from the base, meristem basal. Chromatophores discoid. Plurilocular organs mostly oval, usually equal laterally, generally pedicellate and not in series. Reproductive organs usually low on the thallus.

STRUCTURE AND REPRODUCTION. Hamel, 1939, pp. x–xi.

R87–88   KEY TO THE SPECIES IN THE LOCAL FLORA

1. Thalli minute, less than 1 mm. tall................................ 2
1. Thalli 1–2 mm. tall... 3
   2. Growing in conceptacles and cryptostomata
     of *Fucus*..........................*F. ellipticus* (p. 87; below)
   2. Growing within conceptacles of
     Cystoseira.....................*F. acuminatus* (p. 88; below)
3. Plurilocular organs cylindrical and
   pedicellate ....*F. cylindricus* (p. 87; below)
3. Plurilocular organs subcylindrical to narrowly
   ovoid, sessile.......................*F. chitonicola* (p. 88; below)

NC88   **Feldmannia chitonicola** (Saunders) Levring
FIG. 4

> Levring, 1960, p. 15.
> *Ectocarpus chitonicola* Saunders, 1898, p. 150; pl. 15, figs. 1–4. Setchell and Gardner, 1925, p. 436. Smith, 1944, p. 88.

NC87   **Feldmannia ellipticus** (Saunders) Hollenberg and Abbott, new comb.

> Basonym: *Ectocarpus ellipticus* Saunders, 1898, p. 149; pl. 14, figs. 6–9. Setchell and Gardner, 1925, p. 436. Smith, 1944, p. 87.

NC88   **Feldmannia acuminatus** (Saunders) Hollenberg and Abbott, new comb.

> Basonym: *Ectocarpus acuminatus* Saunders, 1898, p. 149; pl. 14, figs. 1–5. Setchell and Gardner, 1925, p. 435. Smith, 1944, p. 88; pl. 11, fig. 6.

Feldmannia cylindricus (Saunders) Hollenberg and Abbott, new comb. NC87

Basonym: *Ectocarpus cylindricus* Saunders, 1898, p. 150; pl. 16.
Ectocarpus cylindricus Saunders, Setchell and Gardner, 1925, p. 432. Smith, 1944, p. 87; pl. 12, figs. 1–2 (including synonymy).

Order DICTYOTALES 100

Family DICTYOTACEAE 101

Dictyota binghamiae J. G. Agardh NC101

J. G. Agardh, 1894, p. 72. Dawson, 1950*A*, p. 268 (not *Dictyota binghamiae* J. G. Agardh of Phyc. Bor.-Amer. No. 1392; Setchell and Gardner, 1925, p. 652).
Dictyota flabellata (Collins) Setchell and Gardner, 1924, p. 12. Setchell and Gardner, 1925, p. 652; pl. 34, fig. 3; pl. 35, fig. 7; pl. 36, figs. 13–17; with respect to Monterey specimens only. Smith 1944, p. 101, pl. 15, fig. 6.
Dilopus flabellatus Collins *in* Phyc. Bor.-Amer. No. 834.
Dictyota cribrosa Setchell and Gardner, 1930, p. 147. Dawson, 1950, p. 88.

LOCAL DISTRIBUTION (additional). At the —1.0-foot tide level, near Malpaso Creek. Subtidally from 15 to 125 feet, at Mission Point; Carmel Submarine Canyon; one-half mile south of Carmel Highlands; and near Soberanes Point.

Class HETEROGENERATAE 102

Order DESMARESTIALES 118

Family DESMARESTIACEAE 118

Desmarestia Lamouroux, 1813

REVISED KEY TO THE SPECIES IN THE LOCAL FLORA R119

1. Thalli leaf-like, unbranched...................*D. tabacoides* (below)
1. Thalli branched.. 2
  2. Branches narrow (less than 3 mm. broad)...................... 3
  2. Branches relatively broad (over 5 mm. broad)................. 5
3. Branching opposite 4
3. Branching alternate...................*D. latifrons* (p. 120; below)
  4. Branches hair-like, less than 0.5 mm. broad.*D. viridis* (p. 119; below)
  4. Branches flattened, about 2 mm. broad....*D. linearis* (p. 120; below)
5. Branches 0.5–2.0 cm. broad....................*D. herbacea* (p. 121)
5. Branches 2–10 cm. broad.......................*D. munda* (p. 121)

Desmarestia viridis (Müller) Lamouroux NI119

LOCAL DISTRIBUTION. Subtidally at 125 feet, south of Carmel Highlands. Cast ashore at the south end of Carmel Beach.
PACIFIC COAST DISTRIBUTION. Discontinuous: British Columbia, Washington, northern California, and the Monterey Peninsula.

NI120 **Desmarestia linearis** Gardner *in* Smith

Thalli up to 2 meters tall, up to 1 cm. broad.

LOCAL DISTRIBUTION (additional). Cast ashore at the south end of Carmel Beach and at San Jose Creek Beach. Subtidally from 40 feet, on worm tubes in sand, Carmel Submarine Canyon.

NI120 **Desmarestia latifrons** (Ruprecht) Kützing

Thalli up to 2 meters, 3 cm. tall (Middle Reef of Moss Beach).

NA119 **Desmarestia tabacoides** Okamura
FIG. 5

Okamura, 1909, p. 187, pl. 38.

Thalli large, leaf-like, with 1 or more blades arising from a short stipe, and expanding into broad-oval to subcordate blades, up to 34 cm. tall by up to 21 cm. broad. Blades sometimes irregularly lobed.

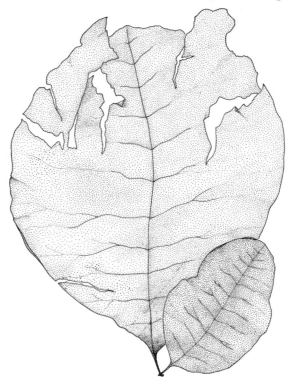

FIG. 5.—*Desmarestia tabacoides.*
Habit of plant. ×¼

Plants chocolate brown, drying to olive or golden brown. Midrib especially prominent at the base of the blades, becoming thinner but remaining clearly marked throughout the length of the blade. Lateral veins opposite, of 7–10 pairs in plants from 40 to 50 feet depth, 15–20 pairs in plants from deeper water (to 100 feet).

LOCAL DISTRIBUTION. Dredged from a depth of 10 fathoms, on shale at south end of Monterey Bay. Subtidally from 40 to 125 feet, off Pescadero Point; Carmel Submarine Canyon; and off Carmel Highlands.

TYPE LOCALITY. Central Japan.

PACIFIC COAST DISTRIBUTION. Monterey region; and subtidally off La Jolla, California.

Order DICTYOSIPHONALES
(= PUNCTARIALES, Smith)

R122

With a macroscopic sporophyte (the species here described) and, where known, a microscopic gametophyte. Sporophytes rarely more than 20 cm. tall, variously shaped as erect, freely branched thalli (such as *Stictyosiphon*) or blade-like (*Punctaria, Halorhipis*), or saccate (*Colpomenia, Soranthera*). Always parenchymatous throughout, with intercalary, apical, or other localized meristems. With unilocular sporangia only, plurilocular sporangia only, or with both kinds of sporangia. The sporangia either remote from one another, grouped in small sori, or completely covering the surface of the thallus. Hairs, either localized or distributed over the thallus, frequently found.

Gametophytes, so far as definitely known, are microscopic, little-branched filaments. (In recent culture studies, however, we have seen the gametophytes of *Soranthera* to exhibit considerable branching.) Gametangia plurilocular and usually uniseriate. Gametic union isogamous or anisogamous. Life histories of few species have been studied, and results are frequently conflicting. Studies of life histories of those species that are restricted epiphytes, such as *Soranthera* and *Coilodesme*, are especially difficult to carry out to completion.

REVISED KEY TO THE FAMILIES IN THE LOCAL FLORA

R123

1. Tips of branches with a uniseriate filament........Striariaceae (p. 132)
1. Tips of branches without a uniseriate filament.................... 2
  2. Growth from a basal meristem..........Scytosiphonaceae (below)
  2. Growth principally intercalary throughout the thallus............ 3
3. Sporangia embedded below thallus surface...Dictyosiphonaceae (below)
3. Sporangia from transformed superficial vegetative
   cells ....Punctariaceae (below)

R123

Family PUNCTARIACEAE

Containing most of the genera Smith included in the Encoeliaceae. Differing from other families in Dictyosiphonales principally in having widespread intercalary divisions in the thallus.

R123

REVISED KEY TO THE GENERA IN THE LOCAL FLORA

1. Sporophyte with solid blades.................................... 3
1. Sporophyte hollow and saccate................................. 2
   2. With reproductive organs grouped in sori.......*Soranthera* (p. 127)
   2. With reproductive organs spread over
      the thallus........................*Colpomenia* (p. 127; below)
3. Internal cells of blade only slightly larger than
   surface cells ....*Punctaria* (p. 123)
3. Internal cells of blade much larger than surface cells............... 4
   4. Blades strap-shaped with pointed apex............*Petalonia* (below)
   4. Blades lanceolate with broad apex............................. 5
5. Reproductive organs grouped in sori.............*Halorhipis* (p. 125)
5. Reproductive organs spread over the thallus....*Phaeostrophion* (below)

NC,R128   ## Colpomenia peregrina (Sauvageau) Hamel

Hamel, 1931–39, p. 201. Blackler, 1963, p. 50.
Colpomenia sinuosa var. *peregrina* Sauvageau, 1927, p. 301.
Colpomenia sinuosa (Roth) Derbès and Solier. Setchell and Gardner, 1925, p. 539; pl. 45, figs. 82–86. Smith, 1944, p. 128; pl. 20, fig. 1 (excluding synonymy).

Thalli, as found on the Monterey Peninsula, growing epiphytically on a variety of algae, as rounded sacs up to 12 cm. in diameter, relatively thin and smooth, and drying to a greenish color. Internally consisting of 1–2 rows of cortical cells and 2–3 rows of subcortical cells. Plurilocular sporangia cover the lower half of the thallus in a continuous layer. Sporangia bifurcate at the tips. Paraphyses numerous, and shorter than the sporangia.

LOCAL DISTRIBUTION. Common everywhere.
TYPE LOCALITY. Atlantic coast of France.
PACIFIC COAST DISTRIBUTION. British Columbia (Vancouver Island) to southern California (La Jolla).

Specimens from sheltered localities like Monterey Harbor and Pebble Beach are larger than those from the open coast. Chiefly distinguished from *C. sinuosa*, which occurs from Santa Catalina Island to La Jolla, California, in being thinner, smoother, and generally of smaller size.

NC130   ## Colpomenia bullosus (Saunders) Yamada

Yamada, 1948, p. 6. Blackler, 1963, p. 50.
Scytosiphon bullosus Saunders, 1898, p. 163; pl. 31, figs. 1–7. Smith, 1944, p. 130.

Colpomenia sinuosa f. *deformans* Setchell and Gardner, 1903, p. 242; pl. 18, figs. 13–15. Setchell and Gardner, 1925, p. 542.

This plant is a locally frequent summer annual. The lack of a basal meristematic zone is the chief reason for excluding it from *Scytosiphon*. This feature, along with the irregularly lobed and saccate form and other detailed features, indicate a relationship with other forms of *Colpomenia*, as treated by Setchell and Gardner.

Petalonia Derbès and Solier, 1850 (nomen conservandum)   NC126

(= Ilea Fries, 1835; Phyllitis Kützing, 1843)

Petalonia debilis (C. A. Agardh) Derbès and Solier   NC126

Derbès and Solier, 1850, p. 265. Silva, 1952, p. 278; p. 299.
Laminaria debilis C. A. Agardh, 1824, p. 120.
Ilea fascia (O. F. Müller) Fries, 1835, p. 321 (*pro parte*). Setchell and Gardner, 1925, p. 535; pl. 44, figs. 68–71, 73. Smith, 1944, p. 126; pl. 20, fig. 4.
Fucus fascia Müller, 1782, p. 7; pl. 768.
Phyllitis fascia (Müller) Kützing, 1843, p. 342; pl. 24, fig. 3. Anderson, 1891, p. 219. Saunders, 1898, p. 161; pl. 30, figs. 1–3.

Phaeostrophion Setchell and Gardner, 1924   NA123

Sporophytes macroscopic, perennial. Thallus with a discoid holdfast up to 20 cm. in diameter, and with one to several ligulate blades. Growth of new blades from a basal meristem. Interior of blade composed of large elongate cells, some becoming thick-walled and filamentous with age; cells at the surface of the blade cuboidal to cylindrical in cross section. With unilocular sporangia only, or with both unilocular and plurilocular sporangia. Both kinds of sporangia distributed over the blades, with two-celled paraphyses associated with the plurilocular sporangia. Spores from both unilocular and plurilocular sporangia producing plethysmothalli, which in turn may produce spores. Plethysmothalli thought to be diploid, with no gametophytes produced in the life history.

STRUCTURE AND REPRODUCTION. Setchell and Gardner, 1925, pp. 585–86; pl. 38, fig. 36; pl. 50, fig. 8; pl. 85. Mathieson, 1965 (Ph.D. thesis, University of British Columbia).

With one species in the local flora.

Phaeostrophion irregulare Setchell and Gardner   NA123

Setchell and Gardner, 1924, p. 10. Setchell and Gardner, 1925, p. 586; pl. 38, FIG. 6
fig. 36; pl. 50, fig. 8; pl. 85. Mathieson, 1965 (Ph.D. thesis, University of British Columbia).

Blades linear to linear-spatulate, often irregularly notched or lobed, 15–25–(40) cm. long, 1.5–4.0 cm. broad. Base gradually attenuate to a slender stipe and discoid attachment. Medulla parenchymatous to somewhat filamentous; cortex thin, 1–3 cells thick. Zoosporangia abundant, more or less ellipsoidal, mostly anticlinally elongate, 38–44 by 24–34 μ, forming a more or less continuous layer at the surface. Gametangia and hairs unknown. A perennial plant varying greatly in size and form.

LOCAL DISTRIBUTION. Locally rare, mostly on sand-swept rocks between the 1.0- and 0.0-foot tide levels. Mussel Point; Pacific Grove; Point Sur.

TYPE LOCALITY. Bolinas, California.

PACIFIC COAST DISTRIBUTION. Alaska (Yakutat Bay); and from British Columbia (Vancouver Island) to southern California (Point Conception).

FIG. 6.—*Phaeostrophion irregulare.* Habit of group of plants. ×⅘

Family SCYTOSIPHONACEAE

Description as for *Scytosiphon* (Smith, 1944, p. 128).

The primary character removing this genus from the Punctariaceae is the possession of a definite basal meristematic area (which, however, *Phaeostrophion* in that family shows). The Punctariaceae are characterized by intercalary divisions throughout the thallus.

With one genus, *Scytosiphon,* in the family.

Family Dictyosiphonaceae

NC,R123, 131

Vegetative construction resembling that of the Punctariaceae, but differing principally in that sporangia are embedded below the thallus surface.

With one genus, *Coilodesme,* in the local flora.

Coilodesme Strömfelt, 1886

KEY TO THE SPECIES IN THE LOCAL FLORA

R131

1. Thallus saccate .... *C. californica* (p. 131)
1. Thallus compressed, never saccate.................. *C. plana* (below)

Coilodesme plana Hollenberg and Abbott

NA131
FIG. 7

Hollenberg and Abbott, 1965, p. 1177; pl. 1, fig. 1.

Plants linear, strictly complanate even when very young, relatively stiff and leathery, up to 58 cm. long and 4–6 cm. broad, with abruptly narrowed base and with margins commonly somewhat ruffled; older plants often longitudinally laciniate above, the divisions frequently with finely dentate and crisped margins; inner tissue of relatively large cells intermixed with abundant filaments extending mostly in a longitudinal direction; sporangia ovoid, 15–20 by 20–26 µ; plants medium to dark brown in color.

LOCAL DISTRIBUTION. Epiphytic on *Cystoseira osmundacea,* on both the basal and reproductive portions. At exposed localities: Asilomar Point; Pescadero Point; Mission Point; Soberanes Point.

TYPE LOCALITY. Soberanes Point.

PACIFIC COAST DISTRIBUTION. Known only from central California: Pigeon Point, San Mateo County; Eagle Glen Canyon mouth, Santa Cruz County; and the Monterey Peninsula.

Differing from *C. californica* in being never sac-like, and in the frequent occurrence of splits in the upper portions.

Order LAMINARIALES

133

Family Laminariaceae

134

Laminaria sinclairii (Harvey *in* Hooker f. and Harvey) Farlow, Anderson, and Eaton

NC135

Farlow, Anderson, and Eaton, 1878, no. 118; Silva, 1957, p. 43. Smith, 1944, p. 135.

Lessonia sinclairii Harvey *in* Hooker f. and Harvey *in* Hooker, 1846.
Hafgygia sinclairii (Harvey *in* Hooker f. and Harvey) Areschoug, 1883.
Laminaria andersonii Eaton *in* Farlow (1876, p. 715, nom. nudum).
Laminaria andersonii Eaton *in* Hervey, 1881, p. 98. Setchell and Gardner, 1925, p. 605. Smith, 1944, p. 137; pl. 21, fig. 1.

Fig. 7.—*Coilodesme plana.* Habit of mature plant, showing laciniate divisions, crenulated margins, and flattened basal area. ×¼

Some specimens collected from near the type locality (Santa Cruz) are nearly 3 meters long.

Laminaria ephemera Setchell   NI136

Some specimens collected from near the mouth of Little Sur River are 2 meters long.

Laminaria setchellii Silva   NC137

Silva, 1957, p. 42.
Hafgygia andersonii Areschoug, 1883, p. 3.
Laminaria andersonii (Areschoug) Farlow *in* Anderson, 1891, p. 220. Smith, 1944, p. 137.
Laminaria andersonii Farlow of Howe, 1893, p. 67. Setchell, 1905A, p. 145; pl. 17, figs. 19–25. Setchell and Gardner, 1925, p. 605. (Not of Eaton *in* Hervey, 1881, p. 98.)

Family LESSONIACEAE

REVISED KEY TO THE GENERA IN THE LOCAL FLORA   R138

1. Stipe in large part prostrate.................................... 2
1. Stipe wholly or in large part erect............................... 3
   2. Blade without a midrib....................*Dictyoneurum* (p. 139)
   2. Blade with a smooth midrib.......*Dictyoneuropsis* (p. 140; below)
3. Blades not borne radially at apex of stipe......................... 4
3. Blades borne radially at apex of stipe..............*Postelsia* (p. 142)
   4. Individual blades each with a pneumatocyst
     at base ....*Macrocystis* (p. 143)
   4. Individual blades lacking pneumatocysts....................... 5
5. Stipe with a single large pneumatocyst below region of
   dichotomous branching 6
5. Stipe without a pneumatocyst.............*Lessoniopsis* (p. 145)
   6. Blades from equal dichotomies..............*Nereocystis* (p. 141)
   6. Blades from unequal dichotomies, therefore
     formed unilaterally ....*Pelagophycus* (below)

Pelagophycus Areschoug, 1881   NA138

Resembling *Nereocystis* in general structure, but with the branches above the pneumatocyst more elongate and splitting unilaterally (forming the "antlers") and bearing blades usually of greater length and breadth than those of *Nereocystis*.

STRUCTURE AND REPRODUCTION. Setchell and Gardner, 1925, pp. 629–31. Parker and Dawson, 1964, pp. 303–7.

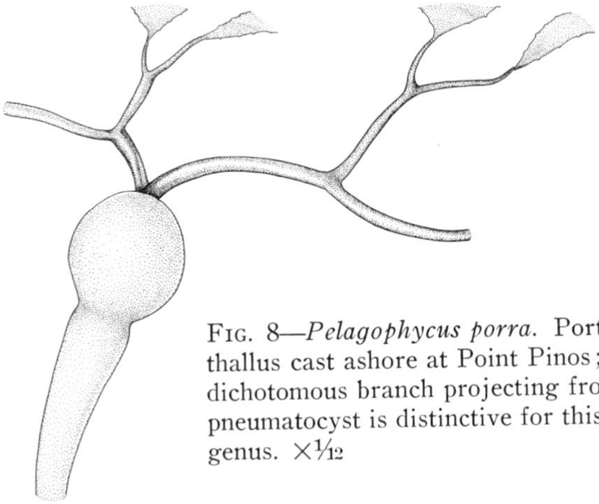

FIG. 8—*Pelagophycus porra*. Portion of thallus cast ashore at Point Pinos; twisted dichotomous branch projecting from pneumatocyst is distinctive for this genus. ×¹⁄₁₂

NA138
FIG. 8

Pelagophycus porra (Leman) Setchell

Setchell, 1908, pp. 129–34. Parker and Dawson, 1964, pp. 303–7.
Laminaria porra Leman, 1822, p. 189.

Haptera confined to a short length of lowermost stipe, not extensive, usually 10–20 cm. broad, usually attached to rock. Stipe solid below, becoming hollow above, 7–27 meters long, terminated by a spherical to subspherical pneumatocyst 10–20 cm. in diameter, and giving rise to 2 solid, flattened to nearly cylindrical branches (the "antlers") each bearing 12–20 blades on the distal side. Blades up to 5.5 meters long and up to 0.4 meter wide, the margins loosely ruffled, more or less beset with small spine-like protuberances. Sori scattered in irregularly shaped areas.

LOCAL DISTRIBUTION. Cast ashore at Point Pinos.
TYPE LOCALITY. Near Santa Catalina Island, California.
PACIFIC COAST DISTRIBUTION. From northern California (Tomales Bay) to Baja California (Punta San Jose), the northern and southern limits representing drifted specimens.

The single specimen we have was taken during the winter, when the northward-flowing Davidson current flows, and may have been carried from the south. See the footnote on p. 138 of Smith.

NI140

Dictyoneuropsis reticulata (Saunders) Smith

LOCAL DISTRIBUTION (additional). Common in the Monterey marina and on the wharf pilings in Monterey Harbor.
PACIFIC COAST DISTRIBUTION. Sonoma County to Santa Cruz; and Santa Rosa Island (Channel Islands), California.

Family ALARIACEAE

Eisenia Areschoug, 1876   NA146

Holdfast of dichotomously branched haptera; stipe elongate and persistent, bifurcate above, the two false branches being the thickened lower margins of the original and subsequently eroded blade. A small partial blade persists at the outer extremity of each false stipe throughout the life of the plant, giving rise to numerous sporophylls along the lower outer margin; perennial. With a macroscopic sporophyte and a microscopic gametophyte.

STRUCTURE AND REPRODUCTION. Setchell and Gardner, 1925, p. 646. Hollenberg, 1938, pp. 34–41.

With one species in the local flora.

Eisenia arborea Areschoug   NA146
                                        FIG. 9

Areschoug, 1878, p. 69. Setchell and Gardner, 1925, pp. 646–47. Smith, 1944, p. 138 (footnote).

Holdfast stout, much branched, with branches intertwined but compact. Stipe nearly terete at the base, becoming much flattened above, 1–2 meters long, rough and rigid, the upper portions containing many mucilage ducts. Blades entire when young, becoming toothed along the margins and corrugate on the surface with age. Sporophylls borne on terminal blades, 30–50 to each blade. Sori irregular in shape, covering most of the surface of each sporophyll. Stipe very dark brown, almost black; blades a golden-olive color.

LOCAL DISTRIBUTION. In subtidal "groves" at depths of 20 to 30 feet, at Whaler's Cove, Point Lobos Reserve State Park.

TYPE LOCALITY. Santa Catalina Island, California.

PACIFIC COAST DISTRIBUTION. Vancouver Island; Monterey region; Santa Catalina Island; and from southern California (Redondo Beach) to Baja California (Isla Magdalena).

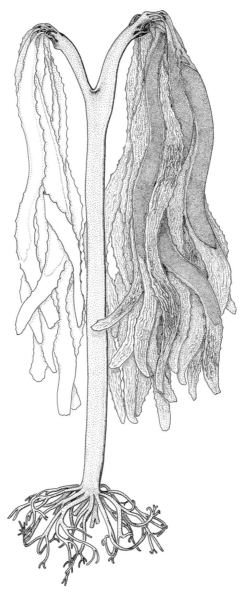

Fig. 9.—*Eisenia arborea.* Habit of thallus of plant taken from 25-foot depth off Whaler's Cove, Point Lobos State Reserve Park; sori occupying nearly the whole of a sporophyll are shown, as are normal corrugated vegetative blades. ×⅛

Previously reported by Setchell as cast ashore at Monterey after severe winter storms, but doubted by Dr. Smith (and by us, until specimens were found attached at Point Lobos).

Egregia laevigata subsp. **borealis** Silva NC150

Silva, 1957, p. 46.
Egregia laevigata f. *borealis* Setchell, 1901, in Phyc. Bor.-Amer., no. XL.
Egregia laevigata Setchell, as interpreted by Smith, 1944, p. 150.

LOCAL DISTRIBUTION. Growing on rocks between the 0.5- and −0.5-foot tide levels. Moss Landing; Monterey Harbor; and Pebble Beach.

TYPE LOCALITY. San Pedro, California (for the species); Pebble Beach, California (for the subspecies).

PACIFIC COAST DISTRIBUTION. Central California (Moss Beach, San Mateo County) discontinuously to southern California (Gaviota, Santa Barbara County).

Class CYCLOSPOREAE 150

Order FUCALES 151

Family FUCACEAE 151

Fucus distichus Linnaeus subsp. **edentatus** (De la Pylaie) Powell NC152

Powell, 1957, p. 424.
Fucus edentatus De la Pylaie, 1829, p. 84 (excluding synonymy). Gardner, 1922, p. 50. Setchell and Gardner, 1925, p. 678.
Fucus furcatus C. A. Agardh, 1820, p. 97. Gardner, 1922, p. 16; pls. 2–3. Setchell and Gardner, 1925, p. 664. Smith, 1944, p. 152; pl. 32, fig. 2 (including synonymy). (Not *F. furcatus* Esper, 1800, p. 178, pl. 95.)
Fucus furcatus f. *luxurians* Gardner, 1922, p. 22; pl. 10. Smith, 1944, p. 152 (see his comment following *F. furcatus*).
Fucus gardneri Silva, 1953, p. 227.

Fucus distichus subsp. **edentatus** f. **abbreviatus** (Gardner) Hollenberg and Abbott, new comb.

NA152
FIG. 10

Basonym: *Fucus furcatus* f. *abbreviatus* Gardner, 1922, p. 19; pl. 6. Setchell and Gardner, 1925, p. 672; pl. 98.
Fucus gardneri f. *abbreviatus* (Gardner) Scagel, 1957, p. 116.

Thalli, as found in the Monterey region, 10–25 cm. tall, regularly dichotomous, with the divisions 1–2 cm. broad and with prominent midrib below. Color olive-brown to dark brown. Receptacles mostly tapering to acute tips, constituting half or more than half of the length of the mature plant, and forming gradual continuations of the branches. Caecostomata abundant. Conceptacles numerous and prominent.

LOCAL DISTRIBUTION. Abundant in the upper littoral zone on a rocky point near the mouth of Carmel River.

TYPE LOCALITY. Waldron Island, San Juan County, Washington.

PACIFIC COAST DISTRIBUTION. Northern Washington to central California (Monterey County).

In view of Powell's (1957, 1957A) well-documented studies on both the systematics and the ecology of the genus *Fucus*, it may be of doubtful value to recognize one of Gardner's many forms of *Fucus furcatus*. However, we believe that the specimens we attribute to f. *abbreviatus* are so strikingly different from the common *Fucus* in this area that recognition of its differences may be in order. Forma *abbreviatus* may be readily recognized by its slender branches, in which half or more than half of the length is occupied by tapering receptacles. The commonest kind of the subspecies in this area may be described as having large, coarse thalli with broad branches and rounded tips (the form that has been described by Gardner as f. *luxurians,* which we do not recognize as distinct).

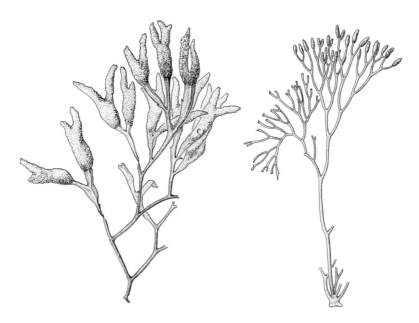

FIG. 10 (*left*)—*Fucus distichus* subsp. *edentatus* f. *abbreviatus.* Habit of specimen from near the mouth of the Carmel River, showing slender branches and tapering receptacles characteristic of this form. ×⅔

FIG. 11 (*right*)—*Pelvetiopsis arborescens.* Habit of thallus. ×1

These may be found in protected localities like Stillwater Cove and Monterey Harbor, as well as at exposed locations like Asilomar Point, Pescadero Point, Mission Point, and Malpaso Creek. Populations from these habitats seem remarkably uniform in appearance.

Pelvetiopsis Gardner, 1910

KEY TO THE SPECIES IN THE LOCAL FLORA   R155

1. Frond slender and very largely terete..........*P. arborescens* (below)
1. Frond wide and very largely compressed..........*P. limitata* (p. 155)

Pelvetiopsis arborescens Gardner

NA155

Gardner, 1940, p. 270; pl. 34.   FIG. 11

Thalli up to 15 cm. tall, strongly arcuate, of a greenish-olive color. Base discoid, the branches arising from it cylindrical for ¼ to ½ their length before becoming somewhat flattened above, dichotomously to subdichotomously branched, rarely more than 3 mm. wide throughout their length, although tapering somewhat near the apices. Receptacles subcylindrical, blunt, usually simple.

LOCAL DISTRIBUTION. On very exposed headlands: Cypress Point; Point Lobos; Yankee Point; rocks near Malpaso Creek; and near Little Sur River.

TYPE LOCALITY. Point Lobos (Point Carmel).

PACIFIC COAST DISTRIBUTION. As above.

A very much taller and more slender species than *Pelvetiopsis limitata*, chiefly distinguished by the terete nature of the branches. Near Malpaso Creek, this species may be found growing near the flattened forms of *P. limitata*, which suggests they are separate species, and not merely ecological variants.

DIVISION RHODOPHYTA

Class RHODOPHYCEAE

159

Subclass BANGIOPHYCIDAE
(= Subclass BANGIOIDEAE, Smith)

NC160

With five orders, two of which (Goniotrichales and Bangiales, below) are represented in the local flora.

R160

KEY TO THE ORDERS IN THE LOCAL FLORA

1. Cells separated by conspicuous gelatinous material; asexual reproduction including direct metamorphosis. . Goniotrichales (below)
1. Cells not widely separated by gelatinous material; asexual reproduction only by monospores. . . . . Bangiales (p. 160; below)

Order GONIOTRICHALES

NC,R160

Thallus filamentous, branched or unbranched; the filaments elongating by means of intercalary meristematic divisions, sometimes becoming polysiphonous by longitudinal divisions. Individual cells lie irregularly in a conspicuous gelatinous material. Sexual reproduction unknown.

With one family in the local flora.

Family GONIOTRICHACEAE

R160

Thalli filamentous, branched, with the cells seriate and separated from one another by gelatinous material. Cells ovoid or cylindrical, uninucleate, each with a single stellate chromatophore with a central pyrenoid (except in *Goniotrichopsis*).

Asexual reproduction by direct metamorphosis of vegetative cells into spores and the spore formation not preceded by cell division, and through naked monospores.

With two genera in the local flora (as in Smith).

Order BANGIALES

R160

Thallus filamentous, disc-like or blade-like. Growth through intercalary horizontal and longitudinal divisions. Cells not widely separated by gelatinous material. Asexual reproduction by monospores. Sexual reproduction by means of spermatia and in some species structures functioning like carpogonia. Reproduction in *Porphyra* also by means of an alternate, heteromorphic phase in the life cycle (*Conchocelis* stage), but details appear to vary with the species, and some details are not yet fully understood.

R160   REVISED KEY TO THE FAMILIES IN THE LOCAL FLORA

1. Bases commonly cushion-like, with no rhizoids from the
     lower cells...........................Erythropeltidaceae (below)
1. Bases not cushion-like, rhizoids from
     lower cells...........................Bangiaceae (p. 166; below)

NC,R162   Family ERYTHROPELTIDACEAE

(ERYTHROTRICHIACEAE, Smith)

Thalli without a definite base, or with a cushion-like base, with no rhizoids from the lower cells. Thalli filamentous or nonfilamentous. Filamentous thalli branched or unbranched. Cells uninucleate and with a single stellate chromatophore.

Asexual reproduction by monospores that are formed through divisions of vegetative cells, and a development of small daughter cells into a sorus.

R162   REVISED KEY TO THE GENERA IN THE LOCAL FLORA

1. Thalli microscopic 2
1. Thalli macroscopic, growing together in close tufts on
     Phyllospadix or *Zostera*.......................*Smithora* (below)
    2. Thallus creeping, of branched filaments in a more or less
       monostromatic disc.....................*Erythrocladia* (p. 165)
    2. Thallus erect, of uniseriate filaments
       (except *E. pulvinata*).................*Erythrotrichia* (p. 162)

NC,R169   **Smithora** Hollenberg, 1959

Plants epiphytic, with several to numerous blades arising from a cushion-like base. Blades monostromatic, without rhizoidal processes from the basal cells. Asexual reproduction by monospores from marginal wart-like sori. Spermatangia cut off singly by a curving wall from the outer ends of pigmented cells in distromatic areas, mostly in median lateral parts of the blades. Characteristic and very gelatinous sori are formed and shed periodically, in connection with series of spring tides, from terminal parts of the blades. The nature and function of these sori is not clear.

STRUCTURE AND REPRODUCTION. Hollenberg, 1959, p. 3, figs. 1–5.

With one species in the local flora.

Smithora naiadum (Anderson) Hollenberg NC169

Hollenberg, 1959, p. 3, figs. 1–5.
Porphyra naiadum Anderson *in* Blankinship and Keeler, 1892, p. 148. Howe, 1893, p. 67. Hus, 1902, p. 212; pl. 21, figs. 19–22. Kylin, 1941, p. 4. Phyc. Bor.-Amer. No. 632. Smith, 1944, p. 169; pl. 40, fig. 1.

Family BANGIACEAE

REVISED KEY TO THE GENERA IN THE LOCAL FLORA R167

1. Thallus filamentous, penetrating old shells........*Conchocelis* (below)
1. Thallus not filamentous, not penetrating shells..................... 2
   2. Thalli cylindrical, growing in masses.............*Bangia* (p. 167)
   2. Thalli blade-like.. 3
3. Blades without a stipe.....................*Porphyra* (p. 168; below)
3. Blades with a stipe.....................*Porphyrella* (p. 175; below)

Porphyra C. A. Agardh, 1824

REVISED KEY TO THE SPECIES IN THE LOCAL FLORA R169

1. Blades monostromatic... 2
1. Blades distromatic 6
   2. Cells with 2 chromatophores............................... 3
   2. Cells with 1 chromatophore............................... 4
3. Thalli saxicolous ....*P. lanceolata* (p. 170)
3. Thalli epiphytic..............................*P. pulchra* (p. 170)
   4. Thalli greenish to steel gray, with some deep
      purple..................................*P. perforata* (p. 172)
   4. Thalli with red and orange-red pigments predominant............ 5
5. Carpospores in packets of 8.....................*P. thuretii* (p. 171)
5. Carpospores in packets of 32.................*P. nereocystis* (p. 171)
   6. Margins of blades strongly twisted and
      ruffled in carposporic plants..............*P. schizophylla* (p. 173)
   6. Margins of blades simple................................. 7
7. Carpospores in packets of 16 or 32.......*P. occidentalis* (p. 174; below)
7. Carpospores in packets of 4........*P. miniata* var. *cuneiformis* (p. 174)

Porphyra occidentalis Setchell and Hus *in* Hus NC,R173

Hus, 1900, p. 69. Smith, 1944, p. 174; pl. 39, fig. 1.
Porphyra variegata (Kjellman) Kjellman *in* Hus, 1900, p. 69. Hus, 1902, p. 225; pl. 21, fig. 18. (As applied to West Coast specimens.) Smith, 1944, p. 173; pl. 38, fig. 3. (As applied to Monterey Peninsula specimens.)
Not *Diploderma variegatum* Kjellman 1889, p. 33; pl. 2, figs. 1–4.

Thalli, as found in the Monterey region, mostly 25–40 cm. tall, occasionally up to 110 cm., with lanceolate sessile blades having a broadly rounded base and small discoid holdfast. Apex rounded or sometimes acute, with margins slightly undulate. Blades distromatic, 90–130 μ thick, with subcubical cells 12–15 μ in diameter, with a single stellate chromatophore and laminate gelatinous wall. Plants dioecious, the carposporic plants brick-red to purplish-red, with carpospores in packets of 16–32, intermingled with vegetative cells. Spermatangial plants, previously known in this region as *P. occidentalis,* cerise, 50–100 μ thick. Spermatangia in packets of 64, forming a continuous yellowish margin in upper parts of the plants. Apparently a spring annual.

LOCAL DISTRIBUTION. Subtidally, on rocks or epiphytic, at 30 feet, Point Joe; at 80 to 100 feet, Pescadero Point; at 50 to 60 feet, north end of Carmel Bay; at 15 feet, Mission Point; at 40 feet, Carmel Submarine Canyon. Frequently cast ashore at Asilomar Point; Middle Reef of Moss Beach; Pebble Beach; and south end of Carmel Beach.

TYPE LOCALITY. Carmel Bay, California.

PACIFIC COAST DISTRIBUTION. Southern British Columbia to Central California.

Specimens from the northwestern Pacific (northern Hokkaido and the Kurile Islands) are smaller and more delicate than our specimens, and in their anatomy appear to resemble the type specimen of *Porphyra variegata* (Kjellman) Kjellman *in* Hus more than our specimens. Previously, we had believed *P. occidentalis* to be nothing more than the male plants of *P. variegata,* but our studies of the Japanese specimens suggest placing all specimens of the two species from the eastern Pacific under the next available name, *P. occidentalis,* and excluding *P. variegata,* as interpreted by various authors, from the Pacific Coast.

NA169   ## Conchocelis Batters, 1892*A*

Thalli microscopic, forming small, irregular, light-pink patches up to 2 cm. in diameter on shells, and composed of branched, creeping filaments that penetrate the shell. Penetrating filaments inflated at intervals, to produce fertile cell rows bearing spores (conchospores) that give rise directly or indirectly to new plants.

STRUCTURE AND REPRODUCTION. Drew, 1956, pp. 553–611 (a summary). Hollenberg, 1958*A,* pp. 653–56 (as applied to the life history of *Porphyra perforata*).

With one species in the local flora.

NA169 ### Conchocelis rosea Batters

Batters, 1892*A,* p. 25.

Description as for the genus.

LOCAL DISTRIBUTION. On old shells of *Mytilus* in tide pools, between the 2.0- and 1.0-foot tide levels, at Mussel Point; and on shells of a large variety of bivalves, dredged from depths of 8–10 fathoms, on shale at south end of Monterey Bay.

TYPE LOCALITY. England.

PACIFIC COAST DISTRIBUTION. Northern Washington; and the Monterey region.

Conchocelis rosea is known as an alternate phase in the life history of *Porphyra umbilicalis* in England, and a phase in a variety of species of *Porphyra* in Japan. Other species of *Porphyra* have been found in culture to have *Conchocelis* stages. In the two local species that have been cultured (*P. perforata* and *P. lanceolata*), the *Conchocelis* stages are essentially alike and little different from those of other species that have been cultured.

Porphyrella gardneri Smith and Hollenberg   NI175

LOCAL DISTRIBUTION (additional). Middle Reef of Moss Beach; south end of Carmel Beach; Malpaso Creek; Little Sur River.

PACIFIC COAST DISTRIBUTION. Oregon; California (Cape Mendocino; Duxbury Reef, Marin County; Davenport, Santa Cruz County; and Monterey County).

Not common, but abundant where found, usually growing on blades of *Laminaria setchellii*.

Subclass FLORIDEOPHYCIDAE   NC176
(= Subclass FLORIDEAE, Smith)

REVISED KEY TO THE ORDERS IN THE LOCAL FLORA   R177

1. Life cycle usually without a free-living
   tetrasporophyte......................Nemalionales (p. 177; below)
1. Life cycle usually with a free-living tetrasporophyte................ 2
   2. Gonimoblast growing from a fusion cell that includes the
      carpogonium........................Gelidiales (p. 192; below)
   2. Gonimoblast growing from a nutritive cell, a connecting
      filament, or an auxiliary cell............................... 3
3. Auxiliary cell an intercalary cell in a vegetative filament
   of the thallus........................Gigartinales (p. 256; below)
3. Auxiliary cell not an intercalary vegetative cell.................... 4
   4. Auxiliary cell formed before fertilization...................... 5
   4. Auxiliary cell formed after fertilization and cut off
      directly from the supporting cell of carpogonial
      filament ....Ceramiales (p. 305; below)
5. Auxiliary cell in a specially formed branch, or is a cell clearly
   modified from a special branch system..Cryptonemiales (p. 198; below)
5. Auxiliary cell the terminal cell of a 2-celled filament borne on the
   supporting cell of carpogonial filament.Rhodymeniales (p. 293; below)

Order NEMALIONALES

NC178   Family ACROCHAETIACEAE

(= CHANTRANSIACEAE, Smith)

Several changes have been made in the taxonomy of *Acrochae-tium* and *Rhodochorton,* necessitating changes in the nomenclature of some of the species listed by Smith. Generally speaking, species showing a few to many small chromatophores are placed in *Rhodo-chorton,* whereas those containing 1 to few band-shaped, plate-like or stellate chromatophores are placed in *Acrochaetium.* Using this criterion, there are far more species of *Acrochaetium* than of *Rhodo-chorton.*

Acrochaetium Nägeli, 1862

6. Penetrating portion forming a branched
   reticulum.............................*A. macounii* (p. 181)
7. Endophytic portion unbranched...........*A. obscurum* (p. 184; below)
7. Endophytic portion branched.........*A. subimmersum* (p. 185; below)
   8. Erect filaments with branchlets opposite or pectinate........... 9
   8. Erect filaments with branchlets alternate..................... 10
9. Thalli with slender branches, chromatophore
   stellate.............................*A. microscopicum* (below)
9. Thalli with stout branches, chromatophore
   parietal............................*A. plumosum* (p. 180; below)
   10. Base of plant disc-shaped.............*A. daviesii* (p. 184; below)
   10. Base of plant creeping....................*A. variabile* (p. 179)

Acrochaetium amphiroae (Drew) Papenfuss

NA178

Papenfuss, 1945, p. 312. Dawson, 1953, p. 27.
Rhodochorton amphiroae Drew, 1928, p. 179; pl. 40, figs. 34–37.
Not *Rhodochorton amphiroae* of Smith, 1944, p. 183; pl. 40, figs. 5–7, which is *Callithamnion lejolisea* Farlow.

Thalli 1–2 mm. high, dark red, growing in the genicula of articulated corallines (usually *Calliarthron*) and sometimes mixed with *Callithamnion lejolisea*. Erect filaments, external to the host, tufted, the cells 10–12 μ wide and 20–24 μ long, irregularly to pectinately branched. Chromatophores parietal. Internal portions creeping between the uncalcified cells of the host, remaining uniseriate and filamentous; original basal spore occasionally seen. Monosporangia terminal or lateral on 1- to 2-celled pedicels, borne in clusters.

LOCAL DISTRIBUTION. Point Pinos; Asilomar Point.
TYPE LOCALITY. White's Point, San Pedro, California.
PACIFIC COAST DISTRIBUTION. Monterey Peninsula; San Pedro, California; Pacific Baja California.

Acrochaetium plumosum (Drew)
(New illustration prepared.)

NI180
FIG. 12

Acrochaetium rhizoideum (Drew)
(New illustration prepared.)

NI180
FIG. 13

Acrochaetium daviesii (Dillwyn) Nägeli

NC184
FIG. 14

Nägeli, 1861, p. 405, figs. 26–27. Papenfuss, 1945, p. 308.
Rhodochorton daviesii (Dillwyn) Drew, 1928, p. 172. Smith, 1944, p. 184 (including synonymy).

Acrochaetium obscurum (Drew) Papenfuss

NC184

Papenfuss, 1945, p. 316.
Rhodochorton obscurum Drew, 1928, p. 193; pl. 48, fig. 87. Smith, 1944, p. 184.

Fig. 12 (*left*)—*Acrochaetium plumosum*. Habit of thallus, showing uni-lateral and bilateral branching. (Rule represents 30µ.)

Fig. 13 (*right*)—*Acrochaetium rhizoideum*. Habit of thallus growing on *Codium*. (Rule represents 30µ.)

NC185   **Acrochaetium subimmersum** (Setchell and Gardner) Papenfuss

Papenfuss, 1945, p. 319.
Rhodochorton subimmersum Setchell and Gardner, 1903, p. 347; pl. 17, fig. 12.
Smith, 1944, p. 185 (including synonymy).

NA178   **Acrochaetium microscopicum** (Nägeli) Nägeli
Fig. 15

Nägeli, 1861, p. 173.
Callithamnion microscopicum Nägeli *in* Kützing, 1849, p. 640.
Rhodochorton microscopicum (Nägeli) Drew, 1928, p. 163.
Kylinia microscopica (Nägeli) Kylin, 1944, p. 13.
Chromastrum microscopicum (Nägeli) Papenfuss, 1945, p. 322.

Plants 1–1.5 mm. tall, epiphytic, with a creeping disc-like base wholly superficial to the host, producing 1–2 short, little-branched filaments, terminating in a colorless, pointed hair. Branchlets opposite, or occasionally secund. Cells of the branchlets somewhat moniliform, about 8 μ in diameter. Chromatophore stellate. Monosporangia terminal and lateral on the branchlets, about 8 μ in diameter.

LOCAL DISTRIBUTION. Cast ashore east of Mussel Point on *Botryocladia*.

TYPE LOCALITY. North Atlantic.

PACIFIC COAST DISTRIBUTION. Monterey Peninsula; La Jolla, California.

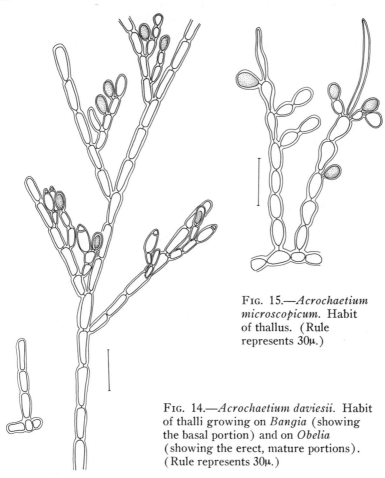

FIG. 15.—*Acrochaetium microscopicum.* Habit of thallus. (Rule represents 30μ.)

FIG. 14.—*Acrochaetium daviesii.* Habit of thalli growing on *Bangia* (showing the basal portion) and on *Obelia* (showing the erect, mature portions). (Rule represents 30μ.)

Acrochaetium desmarestiae Kylin

NA178

Kylin, 1925, p. 10, figs. 4*a–f.*
Rhodochorton desmarestiae (Kylin) Drew, 1928, p. 168; pl. 38, fig. 16.

Thalli epi-endophytic in *Desmarestia munda,* rarely on *D. latifrons,* forming bright-red patches 2–3 cm. in diameter, the basal layer occasionally penetrating the tissues of the host but otherwise creeping over the surface of the host, forming short, erect, rarely branched filaments less than 1 mm. high. Chromatophore plate-like, parietal. Monosporangia 8–10 μ in diameter, sessile or pedicellate, mostly terminal.

LOCAL DISTRIBUTION. Monterey marina; Mussel Point; Point Pinos. Especially abundant in fall and winter, on old plants of *Desmarestia munda* cast ashore.

TYPE LOCALITY. Canoe Island, San Juan Islands, Washington.

PACIFIC COAST DISTRIBUTION. Washington; Oregon (Coos Bay); and Monterey Peninsula.

R181

Rhodochorton Nägeli, 1862

Thalli microscopic to 1 cm. or more in height, with a disc-like or creeping basal portion from which arise few to many branched uniseriate filaments. Cells with few to many discoid chromatophores without pyrenoids.

Asexual reproduction by tetrasporangia, cruciately divided. Sexual reproduction suspected because of spermatangia reported for *R. penicilliforme.*

STRUCTURE AND REPRODUCTION. Papenfuss, 1945, p. 327.

R182   REVISED KEY TO THE SPECIES IN THE LOCAL FLORA

1. Growing on rocks at high-tide level...........*R. purpureum* (below)
1. Growing on hydroids......................*R. concrescens* (p. 183)

(The remaining species listed in Smith have been transferred to *Acrochaetium.*)

NC182 ## Rhodochorton purpureum (Lightfoot) Rosenvinge

Rosenvinge, 1900, p. 75. Papenfuss, 1945, p. 327 (including synonymy).
Rhodochorton rothii (Turton) Nägeli, 1862, p. 121; figs. 1, 3. Smith, 1944, p. 182; pl. 41, figs. 1–2 (excluding synonymy).

NC185   Family NEMALIONACEAE
          (= HELMINTHOCLADIACEAE, Smith)

The order Nemalionales has as its type genus *Nemalion,* which has commonly been placed in the family Helminthocladiaceae. Restoration of the name Nemalionaceae brings a continuity of usage between genus and order.

Nemalion Targioni-Tozetti, 1818 R186

A study of *Nemalion* specimens from the eastern and western north Atlantic, from the Pacific coast of North America, from Japan, and from Australia and New Zealand has convinced the junior author that there is but one species involved. The characters shown by the external vegetative plants, the inner vegetative construction, the formation and appearance of the female reproductive structures (carpogonial branches, sterile cells, gonimoblast initiation, cystocarp), and male reproductive structures show intergrades not only in a given population but between any two or more that are compared. Intergrades sometimes appear even in the same plant. For this reason, we believe that *N. elminthoides* (Velley) Batters is the only species of *Nemalion* that should be recognized.

Nemalion elminthoides (Velley) Batters NC186

Batters, 1902, p. 59. Dawson, 1953, p. 34. Feldmann, 1954, p. 68.
Fucus elminthoides Velley *in* Withering, 1792, p. 255; pl. 17, fig. 2.
Nemalion multifidum (Weber and Mohr) J. G. Agardh, 1841, p. 453.
Nemalion lubricum Duby, 1830, p. 959. Smith, 1944, p. 186; pl. 41, fig. 5.

LOCAL DISTRIBUTION. Widely distributed in Monterey County, but not abundant at the different localities.

TYPE LOCALITY. Isle of Portland, England.

PACIFIC COAST DISTRIBUTION. Alaska (Sitka) to Pacific Mexico.

Magne (1961), in studying the cytology of this species, revealed that there is no meiosis in the zygote, and that the carpospores have twice the number of chromosomes as the cells of the gametophyte. He suggests that the plant that we know as *Nemalion* is but a phase in the life cycle of another alga, probably a tetrasporophyte.

Family CHAETANGIACEAE 189

Pseudogloiophloea Levring, 1953 NC,R189

Resembling *Gloiophloea,* as described by Setchell (1914) and Smith (1944), but possessing colorless utricles.

Pseudogloiophloea confusa (Setchell) Levring *in* Svedelius NC190

Svedelius, 1956, p. 13.
Pseudogloiophloea confusa (Setchell) Hollenberg and Abbott, 1965, p. 1178.
Gloiophloea confusa Setchell, 1914A, p. 118; pl. 14, figs. 44–47. Smith, 1944, p. 190; pl. 42, fig. 1 (including synonymy). Dawson, 1953, p. 48; pl. 4, fig. 2.

Setchell (1914) had based his concept of the genus *Gloiophloea* on a co-type specimen thought to be identical with the type specimen. Levring (1953) found that the two specimens represent two different genera, and therefore proposed the name *Pseudogloio-phloea* for all species that Setchell had placed in *Gloiophloea*. As defined by Levring, only those species possessing utricles should be placed in *Pseudogloiophloea*, those lacking them in *Gloiophloea*. The plant known on the Pacific Coast as *G. confusa* possesses color-less utricles.

191   Family BONNEMAISONIACEAE

NC192   **Bonnemaisonia nootkana** (Esper) Silva

> Silva, 1953, p. 225.
> *Fucus nootkanus* Esper 1802, p. 30; pl. 125.
> *Bonnemaisonia californica* Buffham. Smith, 1944, p. 192; pl. 42, figs. 3–4 (in-cluding synonymy).

> LOCAL DISTRIBUTION (additional). Common in late summer at depths of 50 to 125 feet, at Pescadero Point; Arrowhead Point; in Carmel Sub-marine Canyon; and south of Point Lobos (Point Carmel). Commonly cast ashore, especially in spring and summer, at the south end of Carmel Beach; occasionally also at Moss Beach and west of Fanshell Beach.
> TYPE LOCALITY. Nootka Sound, Vancouver Island.
> PACIFIC COAST DISTRIBUTION. British Columbia to Baja California (Punta San Quintin).

Chihara (1965) has found from local material that this species shows an alternate, microscopic *Traivlliella* stage in its life history.

192   Order GELIDIALES

                         Family GELIDIACEAE

R193   REVISED KEY TO THE GENERA IN THE LOCAL FLORA

1. With one chamber and one ostiole on one side of the
    cystocarp...................................*Pterocladia* (below)
1. With two chambers and two ostioles, one ostiole on each
    side of the cystocarp....................*Gelidium* (p. 193; below)

                   Gelidium Lamouroux, 1813

R194   REVISED KEY TO THE SPECIES IN THE LOCAL FLORA

1. Thallus forming a dark velvety coating on rocks....*G. pusillum* (p. 195)
1. Thallus not forming a dark velvety coating on rocks................2
    2. Thalli less than 5 cm. tall.....................*G. sinicola* (p. 195)
    2. Thalli over 5 cm. tall.......................................3
3. Axis not much broader than finest branches......................4
3. Axis considerably broader than finest branches....................5
    4. Thallus lax, axis clothed with branchlets from base
        to apex.....................................*G. coulteri* (p. 196)

4. Thallus stiff, axis with branchlets only in
      upper third or half.......................*G. setchellii* (below)
5. Axis markedly percurrent.....................*G. robustum* (below)
5. Axis not markedly percurrent................................. 6
   6. Branches diverging widely from axis; with
       few branchlets........................*G. arborescens* (p. 197)
   6. Branches not diverging widely from axis; with
       many branchlets of equal length.........*G. purpurascens* (p. 197)

Gelidium robustum (Gardner) Hollenberg and Abbott   NC196

Hollenberg and Abbott, 1965, p. 1179.
Basonym: *Gelidium cartilagineum* var. *robustum* Gardner, 1927E, p. 280; pl.
54. Smith, 1944, p. 196; pl. 43, fig. 4 (including synonymy).

Comparison with specimens of *Gelidium cartilagineum* (Linnaeus) Gaillon in various herbaria has convinced us that the common West Coast variety *robustum* should be given specific rank. Its erect, unbranched lower axes and its strict and stiff upper branching with pyramidal shape differ from those of *G. cartilagineum*.

Gelidium setchellii Gardner   NA193
                                    FIG. 16

Gardner, 1927E, p. 275; pl. 40, figs. 1–2.

Plant 20(25–35) cm. high, of a purplish-brown color. Erect shoots with a percurrent axis, distichously branched and once pinnate in the upper ½ to ⅓ of the axis, naked below. Main axes up to 1 mm. in diameter, tapering slightly from base to apex. Branches of less than 0.75 mm. diameter throughout, constricted only slightly at their bases. Cystocarps near the outer end of relatively long, simple ramuli. Tetrasporangia in terminal club-shaped ramuli, borne close to the axis. Spermatangia unknown.

LOCAL DISTRIBUTION. Cast ashore at south end of Carmel Beach.
TYPE LOCALITY. Cast ashore at Duxbury Reef, Marin County, California.
PACIFIC COAST DISTRIBUTION. As above.

Differing from *G. purpurascens,* which it resembles more than any other species in the local flora, by the strongly percurrent axes and the small number of branches of second and higher orders.

Pterocladia J. G. Agardh, 1852   NC,R194

Differing principally from *Gelidium* by having a single chamber in the cystocarp, discharging through a single ostiole, whereas *Gelidium* has two chambers and two ostioles.

STRUCTURE AND REPRODUCTION. J. G. Agardh, 1852, p. 482.

With one species in the local flora.

FIG. 16.—*Gelidium setchellii*. Habit of tetrasporangial thallus, showing small number of lateral branches characteristic of the species. ×1

Pterocladia caloglossoides (Howe) Dawson NC194

Dawson, 1953, p. 76.

Gelidium caloglossoides Howe, 1914, p. 96; pl. 35, figs. 1–12. Hollenberg, 1942, p. 534. Smith, 1944, p. 194; pl. 44, figs. 3–4.

Pterocladia parva Dawson, 1953, p. 77 (with respect to Monterey Peninsula specimens).

Order CRYPTONEMIALES R198

Thalli monoaxial or multiaxial; rarely filamentous, generally nonfilamentous and either erect or crustose. Erect thalli cylindrical to foliaceous, branched or unbranched. With vegetatively identical gametophyte and tetrasporophyte.

Spermatangia in open clusters, in sori or borne in conceptacles. Carpogonial filaments from 2 to a dozen or more cells in length, branched or unbranched; remote from one another or adjoining one another, and borne either separately, or in sori, or in nemathecia, or in conceptacles. Carpogonial branches specially formed—i.e., not co-equal with vegetative branches, and initiated at a different time than vegetative branches. The gonimoblast filaments growing from auxiliary cells borne in special auxiliary filaments adjacent to or remote from carpogonial filaments, or the gonimoblast filaments issuing from connecting (oöblast) filaments, or cells directly associated with the carpogonial filaments. All auxiliary cells formed on an auxiliary cell branch, or a clearly derived and modified branch. Cystocarps usually deeply embedded in thallus, relatively small, mostly without a special envelope, but, in the Corallinaceae, in conceptacles.

Tetrasporophytes with tetrasporangia remote from one another or grouped in sori, nemathecia, or conceptacles. The tetrasporangia zonately or cruciately divided. Not all species have tetrasporophytes.

Revised Key to the Families in the Local Flora R198

1. Thalli crustose, in whole or in part................................ 2
1. Thalli erect, cylindrical or compressed........................... 3
   2. Thalli crustose only; without procarps,
       with nemathecia.................Squamariaceae (p. 211; below)
   2. Thalli crustose except when fertile, then with erect protuberances;
       with procarps, without nemathecia....Dermocorynidaceae (below)
   2. Thalli crustose or erect, with
       conceptacles.....................Corallinaceae (p. 217; below)
3. Carpogonium fusing with one or more cells of its branch
   before production of a gonimoblast.....Dumontiaceae (p. 199; below)
3. Carpogonium not fusing with one of the cells of its branch........... 4

NOTE: The Family Cruoriaceae has been removed to the Order Gigartinales by Kylin (1956). See the revised key on p. 83 of this Supplement.

R199   Family DUMONTIACEAE

This family differs from all others in this order in that the fertilized carpogonium fuses with one of the cells on its branch directly or by means of extensions before the oöblast (connecting) filament is formed on its way to the auxiliary cell in a different branch system. The cell with which the carpogonium fuses is referred to as a nurse cell or nutritive cell.

R199   REVISED KEY TO THE GENERA IN THE LOCAL FLORA

R203   Farlowia J. G. Agardh, 1876

Thalli erect, solitary or in clusters from a small disc-shaped base. Erect portions freely branched. Branches with a single axial filament formed by a dome-shaped apical cell. Each segment of the axis producing four laterals, the two first-formed contributing more than the later-formed ones to the bulk of the flattened thallus. Axial filament and lower orders of laterals enveloped by rhizoidal filaments that fill the medulla. Cortex composed of 8–12-celled branched filaments, laterally apposed and smaller at the surface than at the medulla.

Spermatangia formed superficially by surface cells. Carpogonial and auxiliary cell branches formed on the inner cortical cells, remote from each other. Carpogonial branches curved, of 10–18 cells arranged so that the terminal 4–5 cells are strongly recurved on the lower ones. One of the proximal enlarged cells will serve as a nutritive cell. After fertilization, the carpogonium fuses, by means of an extension, without cross walls, with one of the nutritive cells. A further extension, the oöblast (connecting) filament grows to and connects with one or more auxiliary cells. Auxiliary cell branches 9–14 cells, of which an intercalary cell serves as the functional auxiliary cell. After fusion with the oöblast filament, a gonimoblast is produced from the auxiliary cell. All but the lowermost cells become carposporangia. Cystocarp globose, embedded in the thallus in groups, and slightly raising the thallus surface.

Tetrasporophytes unknown.

STRUCTURE AND REPRODUCTION. Abbott, 1962, pp. 29–37; figs. 1–12.

Farlowia mollis (Harvey and Bailey) Farlow and Setchell NC204, 205

Smith, 1944, p. 204; pl. 47, fig. 5 (including synonymy).
Farlowia crassa J. G. Agardh, 1876, p. 262. Anderson, 1891, p. 222. Smith, 1944, p. 205; pl. 46, fig. 1. *F. crassa* has been placed in synonymy with *F. mollis* by Doty (1947*A*) and by Abbott (1962).

Weeksia reticulata Setchell NI207

LOCAL DISTRIBUTION (additional). Common throughout the year, at depths of more than 20 feet, off Mission Point and off Point Lobos (Point Carmel); and to 100 feet in Carmel Submarine Canyon.

PACIFIC COAST DISTRIBUTION. At a depth of 50 feet, off Punta Estero, San Luis Obispo County, California; at 80 feet, off Punta Santo Tomas, Pacific Mexico; and from the Monterey Peninsula.

Family GLOIOSIPHONIACEAE R208

Thalli erect, filamentous or nonfilamentous. Nonfilamentous thalli branched, with cylindrical or compressed branches. Thalli monoaxial, with a percurrent axial filament, and with the cortical region loosely compacted and gelatinous. Deciduous colorless hairs common on the surface cells.

Carpogonial and auxiliary cell filaments with a common supporting cell. Carpogonial filament 3–5-celled, usually without laterals. The auxiliary cell filament 3–7-celled, sometimes with laterals, with the auxiliary cell either terminal or intercalary. Immediate post-fertilization phenomena do not include fusion with one of the cells subtending the carpogonium, but involve the production of a connecting filament (in *Gloiosiphonia*), or of a connecting cell (in *Schimmelmannia*), or of direct fusion with the auxiliary cell (*Thuretella*). Cystocarps small, globose, produced in small number, and not noticeably raising the thallus. Nearly all cells of the cystocarp becoming carposporangia. Tetrasporophytes known for some species.

R208

KEY TO THE GENERA IN THE LOCAL FLORA

1. Thallus gelatinous, not compressed, branching whorled or
   irregular...............................*Gloiosiphonia* (p. 208)
1. Thallus lax, compressed, branching distichous and
   opposite ....*Schimmelmannia* (below)

NC,R201

Schimmelmannia Schousboe *in* Kützing, 1847
(= Baylesia Setchell, 1912)

Plants upright, with a strongly developed main axis from which arise richly divided branches of limited growth, with occasional branches of unlimited growth, oppositely placed. All portions of plants uniaxial, the axes surrounded by rhizoids. Cortex filamentous, but tightly branched and compressed; medullary area interspersed by rhizoids. With procarps. The carpogonial branch and auxiliary cell branch borne on the same supporting cell. After fertilization, the carpogonium dividing twice, one of these cells serving as a connecting cell with the adjacent auxiliary cell. Nearly all cells of the cystocarp become carpospores. Spermatangia superficially produced in small patches. Tetrasporophytes unknown.

STRUCTURE AND REPRODUCTION. Kylin, 1930, p. 14; Abbott, 1961, pp. 379–86; pls. 1–2.

With one species in the local flora.

NC,R201 ### Schimmelmannia plumosa (Setchell) Abbott

Abbott, 1961, p. 379; pls. 1–2.
Basonym: *Baylesia plumosa* Setchell, 1912, p. 249; pl. 29. Smith, 1944, p. 201; pl. 45, fig. 1.

Thalli up to 60 cm. tall, but mostly about 10–15 cm. tall, of a dark wine-red color. The axis and major branches 2–4 mm. in diameter, and with short fringing branches of limited growth 1–3 cm. long. Occasional branches of unlimited growth. Plants pinnate or bipinnate from one or more strongly leading axes, the pinnae becoming bushy when the plant is fertile. Regenerative growth at the tips of the plant frequent.

LOCAL DISTRIBUTION. Of infrequent occurrence, as listed by Smith, and never growing in large numbers.

TYPE LOCALITY. Pacific Grove.

PACIFIC COAST DISTRIBUTION. Central California (Moss Beach, San Mateo County) to southern California (Point Conception, Santa Barbara County).

Family ENDOCLADIACEAE

KEY TO THE GENERA IN THE LOCAL FLORA   R210

1. Thallus much branched, covered with short spines...*Endocladia* (p. 210)
1. Branching dichotomous, the thallus smooth.........*Gloiopeltis* (below)

Gloiopeltis J. G. Agardh, 1842   NA210

Thalli erect, growing in small tufts. The branches uniaxial, with the axial filament and surrounding rhizoids frequently degenerating when the plant is mature. Surface cells firmly compacted into a parenchyma, giving the thalli a firm and wiry habit. Carpogonial and auxiliary cell filaments borne in the same branched filament, the carpogonial branches 2-celled and frequently occurring in clusters (polycarpogonial). The auxiliary cell an enlarged cell borne in the same fertile branch system as the carpogonial branches. Cystocarps prominently bulging out the surface of the thallus, nearly all cells becoming carpospores. Tetrasporangia scattered in the outer cortex. Tetrasporophytes slightly taller than cystocarpic plants.

STRUCTURE AND REPRODUCTION. Kylin, 1930, p. 17.

With one species in the local flora.

Gloiopeltis furcata (Postels and Ruprecht) J. G. Agardh   NA210
FIG. 17

J. G. Agardh, 1851, p. 235.

Gloiopeltis minuta Kylin, 1941, p. 7; pl. 2, fig. 4.

Gloiopeltis capillaris Gardner (not of Suringar). Gardner, Phyc. Bor.-Amer. No. 2250.

Thalli up to 5 cm. tall, irregularly dichotomously branched, the tips simple or furcate, brownish-purple in color, drying to nearly black. Thalli growing in low, close tufts. Cystocarps projecting, without spines.

LOCAL DISTRIBUTION. Between the 6.0- and 5.0-foot tide levels, above the *Endocladia* zone: Pescadero Point; mouth of Carmel River; and near Malpaso Creek.

TYPE LOCALITY. North Pacific Ocean.

PACIFIC COAST DISTRIBUTION. Aleutian Islands to Baja California (Punta Eugenio).

We believe that the height of the plants, together with the thickness of the branches, which are the characters Kylin used to separate the species on this coast, are indiscernible when large numbers of collections and large numbers of a given population are compared. For these reasons, we believe there is only one species on the West Coast of North America.

FIG. 17.—*Gloiopeltis furcata.* Habit of thalli. ×2

211

Family SQUAMARIACEAE

Peyssonelia Decaisne, 1841

R212

KEY TO THE SPECIES IN THE LOCAL FLORA

1. Thalli firm and waxy; tetrasporangial sori small
   and circular...............................*P. pacifica* (p. 212)
1. Thalli soft, not waxy; tetrasporangial sori
   extensive and coalescent.....................*P. profunda* (below)

NA212 **Peyssonelia profunda** Hollenberg and Abbott

Hollenberg and Abbott, 1965, p. 1179; fig. 8.

Thalli up to 6 cm. broad, 500–700 μ thick, of tender consistency and only slightly calcified, firmly attached to the substrate by numerous colorless unicellular rhizoids, but the margin loosening on drying; rhizoids 10–12 μ in diameter and 2–4 diameters long, cut off as separate cells. Color dark red when freshly collected, to terra cotta when dried, with distinct radiating lines, especially in dried specimens. Tetrasporangial nemathecia prominently elevated, forming extensive areas 1–2 cm. across or composed of more or less confluent smaller patches; tetrasporangia 40–60 by 80–140 μ among paraphyses composed of 6–9 cells. Male sori only slightly elevated from the surface. Cystocarpic sori elevated like the tetrasporangial sori.

LOCAL DISTRIBUTION. Dredged from depths of 5–10 fathoms, on shale at south end of Monterey Bay.

TYPE LOCALITY. As above, at about 10 fathoms.

PACIFIC COAST DISTRIBUTION. As above.

Tetrasporangial plants far outnumber the sexual plants.

Rhodophysema Batters, 1900   NC213
(= **Rhododermis** Harvey, 1844, and **Rhododermis** Crouan and Crouan *in* J. G. Agardh, 1851)

Rhododermis Harvey (1844) is an earlier name for *Rhododermis* Crouan and Crouan *in* J. G. Agardh (1851), but cannot be used for this group of plants since Harvey in 1849 placed it in synonymy with *Hildenbrandia prototypus* Nardo. The correct name for this taxon is *Rhodophysema*. A revised description of the species follows.

KEY TO THE SPECIES IN THE LOCAL FLORA   R213

1. Thallus wholly monostromatic except where fertile. . . . *R. minus* (below)
1. Thallus polystromatic
    throughout. . . . . *R. elegans* var. *polystromatica* (below)

Rhodophysema elegans var. polystromatica (Batters) Dixon   NC,R213

Dixon, 1964, pp. 70–71.   FIG. 18
Rhododermis elegans f. *polystromatica* Batters, 1890, p. 310.   FIG. 19
Rhododermis elegans Crouan and Crouan *in* J. G. Agardh, 1852, p. 505. Smith, 1944, p. 213.

Plants irregularly circular, up to 5 mm. in diameter or forming extensive crusts, 60–100 µ thick in fruiting areas (including the paraphyses), of a bright rose-red to dark brownish-red in color. Hypothallus monostromatic, of cells about 8 µ wide and high, and 12–16 µ long. Erect filaments of the perithallus firmly cohering, mostly 6–9 cells, 5–9 µ in diameter and somewhat shorter than broad. Paraphyses 45–50(110) µ long, slightly curved, composed of 4–9 cells. Tetrasporangia 13–15 µ broad, 24–40 µ long, cruciate, terminal on the erect filaments.

LOCAL DISTRIBUTION. On stipes of *Cystoseira osmundacea*, at Mussel Point; Mission Point. On small loose rocks, north end and Middle Reef of Moss Beach; rocks near Malpaso Creek.

TYPE LOCALITY. Brest, France.

PACIFIC COAST DISTRIBUTION. Central California (Duxbury Reef, Marin County) to southern California (San Pedro).

The plants growing on *Cystoseira* stipes generally have longer paraphyses, and somewhat thicker crusts, and form more continuous layers.

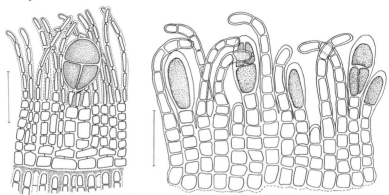

Fig. 18 *(left)*—*Rhodophysema elegans* var. *polystromatica*. Transverse section of thallus, showing monostromatic hypothallus and thicker perithallus characteristic of plants epiphytic on *Cystoseira* stipes. (Rule represents 30μ.)

Fig. 19 *(right)*—*Rhodophysema elegans* var. *polystromatica*. Transverse section of thallus growing on rock. (Rule represents 30μ.)

NA213
Fig. 20

Rhodophysema minus Hollenberg and Abbott

Hollenberg and Abbott, 1965, p. 1181; fig. 9.

Thalli bright red, drying to a dark rose, in thin circular crusts 8–10 mm. in diameter and monostromatic except for fruiting areas; the basal stratum lacking rhizoids. The crusts composed of radiating and forking rows of cells 6–7 μ broad, slightly higher and mostly 1.2–2.0 diameters long. Tetrasporangial sori single and central, about ⅓ the diameter of the discoid thallus, tetrasporangia cruciately divided, 14–16 μ by 15–20 μ on pedicels among slightly curved paraphyses of 4–5 cells. Sexual plants not seen.

Local Distribution. Dredged from about 7 fathoms off the breakwater at Monterey. Cast ashore on *Pterygophora* sporophylls, Carmel Bay. (The latter specimens are incorrectly referred by Smith to *Rhododermis elegans*.)

Type Locality. On a broken cup, dredged from a depth of about 7 fathoms off the breakwater at Monterey.

Pacific Coast Distribution. As above.

This species differs from previously described species of *Rhodophysema* in the lack of erect filaments cohering to form a distinct perithallus, the monostromatic basal layer constituting the entire vegetative thallus.

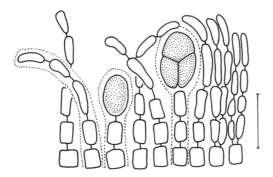

Fig. 20.—*Rhodophysema minus.* Transverse section through a fertile layer, showing tetrasporangia; the thallus when not fertile is monostromatic. (Rule represents 30μ.)

Hildenbrandia occidentalis Setchell   NI215

This is perhaps the most common encrusting alga on the Monterey Peninsula, forming large patches on the sides and sometimes the tops of rocks, the patches being at times several meters square. Fertile tetrasporangial plants show even zonate division of tetrasporangia (with walls parallel).

Hildenbrandia prototypus Nardo   NI215

Dr. Smith (1944, p. 216) questioned his determination of this species because he had not found fertile material. We have fertile material of this bright rose-red species, collected in both summer and winter at Mussel Point and Point Pinos. Tetrasporangia show obliquely divided walls. This is a common species in the Monterey area, although not as common as *H. occidentalis,* and appears to favor the —1.0-foot and lower tide levels.

Family CORALLINACEAE   NI217

L. R. Mason (1953) made significant changes in the systematics of many members of the crustose Corallinaceae. We give some of her changes here. Other changes made by her do not affect the local flora.

REVISED KEY TO THE GENERA IN THE LOCAL FLORA   R218

1. Thalli wholly crustose and prostrate............................ 2
1. Thalli crustose, button-shaped, hemiparasitic
    on corallines...........................*Polyporolithon* (below)
1. Thalli with erect jointed shoots................................ 6

2. Very thick, stony thalli, commonly found covering rocks and shells 3
2. Thin crusts of small diameter, commonly found epiphytic
on other algae and marine plants............................ 4
3. Tetrasporic conceptacles with a single
pore.............................*Lithophyllum* (p. 226; below)
3. Tetrasporic conceptacles with few to many
pores...........................*Lithothamnion* (p. 220; below)
4. Thalli overgrowing each other, sporangial conceptacles
with a single pore.....................*Dermatolithon* (below)
4. Thalli never superimposed................................. 5
5. Heterocysts absent, sporangial conceptacles with a
single pore...............................*Heteroderma* (below)
5. Heterocysts present, sporangial conceptacles with several
to many pores...............................*Melobesia* (p. 218)
6. Conceptacles restricted to terminal intergenicula................. 7
6. Conceptacles on terminal and intercalary intergenicula........... 8
7. Thallus of many erect articulations, only one conceptacle on the
terminal intergeniculum..................*Corallina* (p. 228; below)
7. Thallus of one or two erect articulations, one or rarely two
conceptacles on the terminal intergeniculum......*Yamadaea* (below)
8. Fertile intergenicula cylindrical or slightly
compressed...............................*Lithothrix* (p. 231)
8. Fertile intergenicula markedly compressed..................... 9
9. Conceptacles borne on both margins and flattened
faces...............................*Calliarthron* (p. 236; below)
9. Conceptacles borne on flattened faces of the intergenicula......... 10
10. Two to eight conceptacles on a flattened face.....*Bossiella* (below)
10. Two conceptacles on axial intergenicula, usually one
on a branchlet........................*Serraticardia* (below)

Lithothamnion Philippi, 1837

REVISED KEY TO THE SPECIES IN THE LOCAL FLORA

1. Thalli growing on rocks, loosely attached.......*L. lamellatum* (p. 222)
1. Thalli growing on rocks, firmly attached......................... 2
2. Upper surface smooth or almost smooth.....*L. californicum* (p. 221)
2. Upper surface not smooth................................... 3
3. Upper surfaces with low outgrowths.......................... 4
3. Upper surfaces with irregular, branched outgrowths............... 5
4. Outgrowths angular but low...............*L. aculeiferum* (below)
4. Upper surface with irregular protuberances
3 or more mm. high...................*L. phymatodeum* (below)
5. Protuberances rounded and cylindrical..........*L. pacificum* (p. 221)
5. Protuberances erect, coralloid, compressed....*L. montereyicum* (p. 222)

Lithothamnion aculeiferum Mason

Mason, 1953, p. 326.

Crust firmly attached to rocks of various sizes, often completely surrounding small pebbles washed about by surf, pinkish-purple when fresh, often drying to a dull purplish-gray. Thalli 1–3 mm. thick, excrescences numerous, angular but low, 1–1.5 mm. high, 1–2.5 mm. wide at base, often tapering to a sharp apex. Hypothallium poorly or irregularly developed. Perithallium 1–2.5 mm. thick, often banded owing to slight differences in size of cells in different regions, cells isodiametric, or slightly elongate or flattened; epithallium monostromatic or distromatic, cells often very flat and usually crushed. Sporangial conceptacles 140–165 μ in diameter, usually somewhat flattened periclinally, roof convex, perforated by 15–40 pores. Cystocarpic conceptacles convex, 425–500 μ in diameter. Spermatangial plants unknown.

LOCAL DISTRIBUTION. Pacific Grove, California.
TYPE LOCALITY. White's Point, San Pedro, California.
PACIFIC COAST DISTRIBUTION. Central California (Marin County) to Baja California (Scammon Lagoon).

Lithothamnion phymatodeum Foslie   NA220

Foslie, 1902, p. 3. Mason, 1953, p. 327.

Thalli indefinite in growth, covering stones, shells, or other algae, reddish-purple when fresh and usually retaining color when dry, thin and brittle, 0.3–2 mm. thick, very irregularly developed. Protuberances 3 mm. or more high, up to 4 mm. in diameter, very irregular; hypothallium well developed, 300–500 μ thick, filaments of cells spreading both upward and downward; perithallium 300–500 μ thick, cells nearly isodiametric or slightly elongated; epithallium 1–3 layers of cells thick, cells flattened periclinally. Sporangial conceptacles convex, forming conspicuous patches, conceptacles 275–350 μ in diameter, 120–170 μ high, roof perforated by 25–40 pores.

LOCAL DISTRIBUTION. Mussel Point; Point Pinos; Pacific Grove.
TYPE LOCALITY. On rocks in upper sublittoral zone, Whidbey Island, Washington.
PACIFIC COAST DISTRIBUTION. Washington (Whidbey Island) to central California (Pacific Grove).

Polyporolithon L. R. Mason, 1953   NC,R222

Thallus hemiparasitic on various corallines, consisting of a foot that penetrates the tissue of the host, and an expanded, flattened, circular upper part or disc of limited growth. A stalk connecting the foot and disc may be present or the disc may be sessile, appearing to adhere tightly to the host. Conceptacles occur on the upper surface of the disc. Sporangial conceptacles perforated by 5 to 70

pores; cystocarpic and spermatangial conceptacles with but one pore.
STRUCTURE AND REPRODUCTION. Mason, 1953, p. 316.

R222   KEY TO THE SPECIES IN THE LOCAL FLORA

1. Sporangial conceptacles with convex roof perforated by
    30–70 pores................................*P. conchatum* (below)
1. Sporangial conceptacles with roof slightly convex,
    perforated by 5–35 pores......................*P. parcum* (below)

NC222   **Polyporolithon conchatum** (Setchell and Foslie) Mason

Mason, 1953, p. 317.
Lithothamnion conchatum Setchell and Foslie *in* Foslie, 1902, p. 6. Smith,
1944, p. 222; pl. 50, fig. 2 (including synonymy).

Description as for *Lithothamnion conchatum* (Smith, p. 222),
except for the number of pores in the sporangial conceptacles.

This species bears, on its lower surface, the fungus parasite,
Mycophycophila polyporolithi Bonar.

NC223   **Polyporolithon parcum** (Setchell and Foslie) Mason

Mason, 1953, p. 318.
Lithothamnion parcum Setchell and Foslie *in* Foslie, 1907*A*, p. 14. Smith,
1944, p. 223 (including synonymy).

Description as for *Lithothamnion parcum* (Smith, p. 223), except for the number of pores in the sporangial conceptacles.

NC223   **Fosliella** Howe, 1920

Of the four species of *Fosliella* in Smith (pp. 224–26), three
have been transferred to *Dermatolithon* (and two of these placed in
synonymy), and one to *Heteroderma*. As understood by Mason
(1953), there are no species of *Fosliella* in the local flora.

NC,R224   **Dermatolithon** Foslie, 1898

Thallus epiphytic or epizoic, pink to purple, circular or irregular
in outline, two to several layers of cells thick, often encircling host.
Thalli overgrowing one another. Hypothallium monostromatic or
distromatic, cells obliquely elongate; cells of perithallium in section
quadrate or vertically elongate; cells of epithallium small, and quadrate, rectangular, or triangular in section. Sporangial conceptacles
slightly to markedly convex, opening by a single pore, sporangia
scattered over floor of conceptacle or restricted to its periphery.
Cystocarpic conceptacles convex, carpospores arising from periphery of floor; antheridial conceptacles convex.

STRUCTURE AND REPRODUCTION. Mason, 1953, p. 342.

KEY TO THE SPECIES IN THE LOCAL FLORA (after Mason)   R224

1. Sporangial conceptacles not bulging above surface
of thallus.....................................*D. dispar* (below)
1. Sporangial conceptacles bulging above surface
of thallus...............................*D. ascripticium* (below)

Dermatolithon ascripticium (Foslie) Setchell and Mason   NC224

Setchell and Mason, 1943, p. 96. Mason, 1953, p. 344.
Lithophyllum pustulatum f. *ascripticium* Foslie, 1906.
Fosliella ascripticia (Foslie) Smith, 1944, p. 224; pl. 50, fig. 7 (including synonymy). Mason, 1953, p. 344.
? *Fosliella intermedia* (Foslie) Smith, 1944, p. 226. Mason, 1953, p. 345.

Dermatolithon dispar (Foslie) Foslie   NC225

Foslie, 1909. Mason, 1953, p. 343.
Lithophyllum tumidulum f. *dispar* Foslie, 1907*A*, p. 27.
Fosliella dispar (Foslie) Smith, 1944, p. 225; pl. 50, fig. 6 (including synonymy). Mason, 1953, p. 343.

Heteroderma Foslie, 1909   NC,R225

Thalli epiphytic, oligostromatic, rose-pink in color. Suborbicular when young, irregular when old, adjacent thalli becoming confluent but never superimposed; heterocysts absent, hypothallium composed of one or two layers of isodiametric cells, never palisade-like; sporangia restricted to periphery or borne over entire floor of conceptacle.

STRUCTURE AND REPRODUCTION. Foslie, 1905, pp. 96 and 102. Mason, 1953, pp. 334–35.

As distinguished by Mason, *Heteroderma* species are essentially monostromatic and without heterocysts; *Melobesia* species, although also essentially monostromatic, possess heterocysts.

With one species in the local flora.

Heteroderma nicholsii Setchell and Mason   NC225

Setchell and Mason, 1943, p. 96. Mason, 1953, p. 336.
Fosliella nicholsii (Setchell and Mason) Smith, 1944, p. 225; pl. 50, fig. 8 (including synonymy).

Lithophyllum Philippi, 1837

REVISED KEY TO THE SPECIES IN THE LOCAL FLORA   R227

1. No pronounced excrescences, branches, or
papillae....................................*L. decipiens* (below)
1. Surface excrescences present.................................. 2
    2. Excrescences erect, cylindrical, frequently
branched...........................*L. proboscideum* (p. 227)

NA226   **Lithophyllum decipiens** (Foslie) Foslie

Foslie, 1900, p. 19. Mason, 1953, p. 338; pl. 40.

Distinguished from other species in the local flora by lack of papillae, or other pronounced excrescences, and by having a thallus 150–500 μ thick, firmly attached to substratum along entire lower surface.

LOCAL DISTRIBUTION. Pacific Grove.
TYPE LOCALITY. San Pedro, California.
PACIFIC COAST DISTRIBUTION. British Columbia to Panama.

NA226   **Lithophyllum imitans** Foslie

Foslie, 1909, p. 13. Mason, 1953, p. 340; pl. 43.

Distingiushed from *L. neofarlowii* in the local flora by larger protuberances (2–5 mm. in diameter) and a thicker hypothallium (⅛ the thickness of the thallus). In *L. neofarlowii,* the protuberances are less than 1.5 mm. in diameter and the hypothallium is of 2–3 cell layers. The surface of the thallus of *L. imitans* appears glazed.

LOCAL DISTRIBUTION. Point Lobos (Point Carmel).
TYPE LOCALITY. Pacific Beach, San Diego County, California.
PACIFIC COAST DISTRIBUTION. Central California (San Mateo County) to Baja California.

NC230   **Corallina vancouveriensis** Yendo

Yendo, 1902, p. 719; pl. 54, fig. 3; pl. 55, figs. 1–2; pl. 56, figs. 16–17. Dawson, 1964, p. 542.
Corallina gracilis f. *densa* Collins. Smith, 1944, p. 230; pl. 50, figs. 3–5 (including synonymy).
Corallina aculeata Yendo, 1902, p. 720; pl. 15, fig. 3; pl. 56, figs. 18–19. Dawson, 1964, p. 542.

NA218   **Yamadaea** Segawa, 1955

Thallus consisting of a conspicuous, adherent crust 3–5 cm. or more in extent, giving rise to scattered, very short, erect, segmented branches 2–3 mm. tall. Basal crust marginally lobed, the lobes not free, about 400 μ thick at the margins. Erect branches irregularly and distantly scattered from each other over the surface of the basal

crust, consisting of one (or two?) erect genicula bearing the conceptacles. Conceptacles of all reproductive phases terminal on the
primary intergeniculum.

STRUCTURE AND REPRODUCTION. Segawa, 1955, pp. 241–47.

With one species in the local flora.

Yamadaea melobesioides Segawa

NA218

Segawa, 1955, p. 241.   FIG. 21

Description as for the genus.

LOCAL DISTRIBUTION. Dredged from depths of 8–10 fathoms, on shale
at south end of Monterey Bay.

TYPE LOCALITY. Susaki, Izu province, Japan.

PACIFIC COAST DISTRIBUTION. As above.

Our specimens possess only one erect branch (intergeniculum)
and should be identified with the Japanese species rather than that
from northern Washington, *Y. americanum* Dawson and Steele,
which sometimes has two erect joints. Specimens are of a dark-
violet color.

FIG. 21.—*Yamadaea melobesioides.* Habit of thalli dredged on shale,
showing single erect segments characteristic
of this Japanese species. ×20

Serraticardia (Yendo) Silva, 1957

NA218

Thallus consisting of a crustose base of indefinite extent, with
many erect, branched, jointed, flexible axes; erect axes of calcified
intergenicula and uncalcified genicula; intergenicula broader than

long but without expanded wings; branching regular, branchlets distichous and opposite. Anatomy as in *Bossiella* (*Bossea* in Smith, 1944) and *Corallina*; conceptacles mostly borne laterally on the faces of the intergenicula, usually paired on axial intergeniculae, one toward each lateral margin, single on the pinnae, occasionally terminal.

STRUCTURE AND REPRODUCTION. Silva, 1957, p. 48.

With one species in the local flora.

NA218   **Serraticardia macmillani** (Yendo) Silva

FIG. 22

Silva, 1957, p. 48. Dawson, 1964, p. 541.
Cheilosporum macmillani Yendo, 1902, p. 718; pl. 52, figs. 4–5; pl. 56, figs. 11–14.
Calliarthron pinnulatum Manza, 1937, p. 565. Manza, 1940, p. 268; pl. 3. Silva, 1957, p. 48.

Thalli saxicolous, 4–11 cm. tall, the axes more or less percurrent, nude below and subterete; above with plumose, bi-tripinnate and opposite branches; basal intergenicula cylindrical or a little compressed, 1–3 mm. long, moniliform, 2 mm. broad; intergenicula of main axes compressed cuneate, hexagonal or truncated, usually much shorter than the 2–3 mm. breadth; ultimate pinnules 2–4 mm. long, 1–2 mm. broad.

LOCAL DISTRIBUTION. Pescadero Point; and at the −1.5-foot tide level on rocks, south of the mouth of Carmel River.

TYPE LOCALITY. Port Renfrew, Vancouver Island, British Columbia.

PACIFIC COAST DISTRIBUTION. Alaska to central California; at lower intertidal levels, near Fort Ross; Bodega Head; Pescadero Point; and at mouth of Carmel River.

Superficially resembling *Bossiella plumosa* (*B. frondescens*) but coarser and less densely branched.

NC231   **Bossiella** Silva, 1957

The name *Bossea* is occupied by a genus of Geraniaceae; accordingly the name *Bossea* has been changed to *Bossiella*. The listing below follows the sequence in Smith (pp. 232–36).

NC232   **Bossiella interrupta** (Manza) Silva, 1957, p. 47.

NC233   **Bossiella californica** (Decaisne) Silva, 1957, p. 46.

NC233   **Bossiella frondescens** (Postels and Ruprecht) Dawson

Dawson, 1964, p. 540.
Corallina frondescens Postels and Ruprecht, 1840, p. 20; pl. 40.
Bossea plumosa Manza 1937, p. 46. Manza, 1940, p. 303; pl. 12. Smith, 1944, p. 233; pl. 51, fig. 1. *Bossiella plumosa* (Manza) Silva, 1957, p. 47.

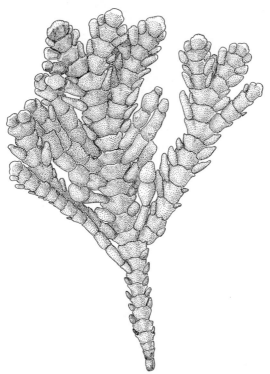

Fig. 22.—*Serraticardia macmillani.* Habit of thallus, showing
distichous branching. ×1½

Bossiella corymbifera (Manza) Silva, 1957, p. 47.   NC234

Bossiella dichotoma (Manza) Silva, 1957, p. 47.   NC234

Bossiella gardneri (Manza) Silva, 1957, p. 47.   NC235

Bossiella orbigniana (Decaisne) Silva, 1957, p. 47.   NC235

Calliarthron Manza, 1937

REVISED KEY TO THE SPECIES IN THE LOCAL FLORA   R237

1. Upper margins of wings of intergenicula with conceptacles.......... 2
1. Upper margins of wings of intergenicula without conceptacles........ 3
   2. Conceptacles on upper margin of wings, lateral margins of
      wings, and on flattened faces..........*C. cheilosporioides* (p. 237)
   2. Conceptacles only on upper margin of wings.....*C. schmittii* (below)
3. Lobes obtuse................................*C. setchelliae* (p. 237)
3. Lobes rounded...........................*C. tuberculosum* (below)

NA237
FIG. 23

Calliarthron schmittii Manza

Manza, 1937, p. 566.

Thallus creeping, repent, with a dorsiventral organization. Branching dichotomous to subdichotomous. Intergenicula somewhat cylindrical at base of shoot, 1–4 mm. long, 1 mm. wide. Intergenicula in upper part of shoot partly compressed, convex, suborbicular to subcordate, with a strong differentiation between wings and midrib, 5–10 mm. long, 5–15 mm. wide. Tetrasporangial conceptacles on upper margin of wings of intergenicula.

LOCAL DISTRIBUTION. In 20 to 25 feet, off Whaler's Cove, Point Lobos.
TYPE LOCALITY. Dredged from depths of 21–24 fathoms off Point Loma (San Diego County).
PACIFIC COAST DISTRIBUTION. As above.

We are grateful to Mr. William Johansen for this record.

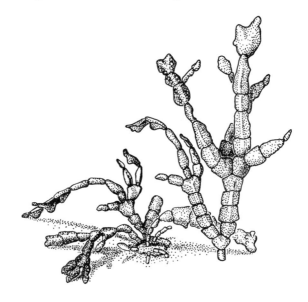

FIG. 23.—*Calliarthron schmittii.* Habit of thallus, showing creeping nature and a dorsiventral organization, the intergenicula being flattened and concave from the top. ×1½

NA237

Calliarthron tuberculosum (Postels and Ruprecht) Dawson

Dawson, 1964, p. 540.
Corallina tuberculosa Postels and Ruprecht, 1840, p. 20; pl. 40.
Calliarthron regenerans Manza, 1937, p. 565. Silva, 1957, p. 48.

Erect shoots 7–15 cm. tall, somewhat delicate, branching generally interruptedly pinnate and opposite. The segments of the branches may be entirely compressed, or the lower portions of the branches may be compressed and their apices cylindrical. Lobes of intergenicula of primary branches rounded. Conceptacles located on the lateral margins and on the faces of the intergenicula.

LOCAL DISTRIBUTION. Partington Point.

TYPE LOCALITY. Moss Beach, San Mateo County, California.

PACIFIC COAST DISTRIBUTION. Alaska to Mexico (Islas Todos Santos).

In size and general shape, resembling *C. setchelliae,* but not as robust as the latter species. Lobes of the intergenicula of *C. tuberculosa* are rounded, those of *C. setchelliae* obtuse.

Family CRYPTONEMIACEAE
(= GRATELOUPIACEAE, Smith)

NC238

The order Cryptonemiales has as its type genus *Cryptonemia,* which has commonly been placed in the family Grateloupiaceae. Use of the name Cryptonemiaceae restores a continuity of usage between genus and order.

KEY TO THE GENERA IN THE LOCAL FLORA

R238

1. Thallus very much branched, stiff to horny..........*Prionitis* (p. 243)
1. Thallus little branched or blade-like, membranous or slimy........... 2
   2. Thallus little branched, but frequently
      proliferous........................*Grateloupia* (p. 238; below)
   2. Thallus principally blade-like............................... 3
3. Blades less than 15 cm. tall, ruffled or lobed, membranous;
   medulla of periclinal filaments..........*Cryptonemia* (p. 240; below)
3. Blades more than 15 cm. tall, simple, usually without ruffles or lobes;
   medulla with some filaments perpendicular to cortex............. 4
   4. Surface of blades like fine-grained leather..*Halymenia* (p. 242; below)
   4. Surface of blades smooth........................*Aeodes* (p. 241)

NOTE: We exclude *Lobocolax* (Smith, 1944, p. 247); they are bacterial galls. NC247

Grateloupia doryphora (Montagne) Howe

NC239

Howe, 1914, p. 169; fig. 43. Dawson, Acleto, and Foldvik, 1964, pp. 49–50 (including synonymy).

Halymenia (?) *doryphora* Montagne, 1839, p. 21.

Grateloupia californica Kylin, 1941, p. 9; text fig. 2B; pl. 1. Smith, 1944, p. 239; pl. 55, figs. 1–2 (including synonymy).

Grateloupia lanceola J. G. Agardh, emend. Ardré and Gayral, 1961, p. 68.

PACIFIC COAST DISTRIBUTION. Puget Sound to Peru (the type locality).

Specimens of this highly variable species that have been collected in the Monterey harbor marina are more than 2 meters tall.

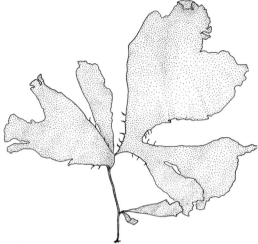

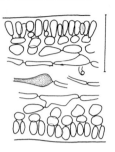

FIG. 24.—*Cryptonemia borealis.* Habit of thallus. ×½

FIG. 25.—*Cryptonemia borealis.* Transverse section of thallus; stippled cell is medullary filament with dense but highly refractive contents. (Rule represents 30μ.)

FIG. 26.—*Cryptonemia obovata.* Habit of thallus. ×⅛

FIG. 27.—*Cryptonemia obovata.* Transverse section of thallus. (Rule represents 30μ.)

Grateloupia setchellii Kylin

NI240

Pacific Coast Distribution (additional). We have recently seen two collections of this species from Humboldt County, California, collected by Michael Wynne and by E. Y. Dawson. The species has been reported from Oregon by Doty. Unlike *G. doryphora*, this species appears to be a spring annual.

More recently collected plants of this entity show them to be up to 37 cm. tall, and with a maximum breadth of the blades of up to 2 cm. These specimens are highly proliferous.

Cryptonemia J. G. Agardh, 1842

KEY TO THE SPECIES IN THE LOCAL FLORA

R240

1. Thallus a simple blade, unbranched, rarely
   lobed.................................*C. ovalifolia* (p. 241; below)
1. Thallus branched, or irregularly lobed............................ 2
   2. Several blades arising from a common base, each digitately
      to simply lobed...........................*C. obovata* (below)
   2. Blades branching from a stipe, each with irregular
      margins but not lobed......................*C. borealis* (below)

Cryptonemia ovalifolia Kylin

NI241
Fig. 28

(New illustration.)

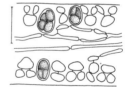

Fig. 28.—*Cryptonemia ovalifolia.* Transverse section of thallus. (Rule represents 30μ.)

Cryptonemia borealis Kylin

NA240
Fig. 24
Fig. 25

Kylin, 1925, p. 19, figs. 8*B–C*, 9.

Thalli blade-like, 12 cm. tall, deep rose-red to cerise in color. Blade deeply divided a short distance from the stipe, which is slightly more than 1 cm. in length. Small proliferations present along the lower edges of the main divisions. Thallus 80–100 μ in diameter, with a narrow cortex, and a medulla of few filaments.

Local Distribution. At 100 feet, in the Carmel Submarine Canyon.
Type Locality. Canoe Island, Washington.
Pacific Coast Distribution. Washington; Oregon (Coos Head); and Monterey Peninsula.

NA240 **Cryptonemia obovata** J. G. Agardh

FIG. 26
FIG. 27

J. G. Agardh, 1876, p. 681.

Thalli blade-like, 15 cm. tall, reddish-brown in color. The firm blade dissected into obovate lobes, frequently asymmetrically formed. One or more blades arising from a stout, flattened stipe 0.5 to 0.75 cm. in diameter, and less than 0.5 cm. in length before expansion into blades. Thallus sections 120 to 150 μ in diameter.

LOCAL DISTRIBUTION. At 100 feet, in the Carmel Submarine Canyon.

TYPE LOCALITY. Golden Gate, San Francisco, California.

PACIFIC COAST DISTRIBUTION. Four reported collections. Others: Prince William Sound, Alaska; Bahia Tortuga, Baja California.

NI243 **Halymenia californica** Smith and Hollenberg

LOCAL DISTRIBUTION. Dredged from depths of 30–35 feet and 60 feet, at the south end of Monterey Bay; and on pebbles and small rocks at 80 to 125 feet, off Pescadero Point. Frequently cast ashore at Point Pinos; Moss Beach; and south end of Carmel Beach.

PACIFIC COAST DISTRIBUTION. Monterey Peninsula; and at a depth of 80 feet, off Punta Santo Tomas, Baja California. Also cast ashore at Punta Maria, Pacific Mexico.

Recent collections of this species (those off Pescadero Point) show that plants may grow to 70 cm. in height.

NA242 **Halymenia schizymenioides** Hollenberg and Abbott

FIG. 29
FIG. 30

Hollenberg and Abbott, 1965, p. 1182; pl. 1, fig. 2; text fig. 10.

Thalli blade-like, broadly lanceolate, and sometimes cleft, up to 46 cm. tall, with or without a short tapering stipe; blade slippery to touch, with a leather-grained surface, brownish-red when fresh, drying to a dark wine-red to rose-red. Thalli 80–100 μ in cross section, the sections showing criss-crossed medullary filaments and a small cortex. Tetrasporangia scattered over the surface, about 30 μ in diameter, produced by outer cortical cells. Cystocarps embedded in and scattered over all parts of the thallus, up to 0.5 mm. in diameter. Spermatangia not seen.

LOCAL DISTRIBUTION. Growing on vertical faces of rocks, between the 1.0- and −1.0-foot tide levels, growing with and under *Iridaea splendens,* and to 15 feet subtidally, at Point Pinos; Pescadero Point; Mission Point; near Point Sur; and near the mouth of Little Sur River. Also cast ashore west of Mussel Point; at Moss Beach; and at the south end of Carmel Beach.

TYPE LOCALITY. Cast ashore at the south end of Carmel Beach.

PACIFIC COAST DISTRIBUTION. As above, and at Davenport, Santa Cruz County.

Differing from *Halymenia californica* in having criss-crossed medullary filaments and by the color and shape of the blades.

Externally resembling *Schizymenia pacifica,* but lacking the gland cells of the latter and having blades lanceolate instead of sub-cordate as in *S. pacifica.*

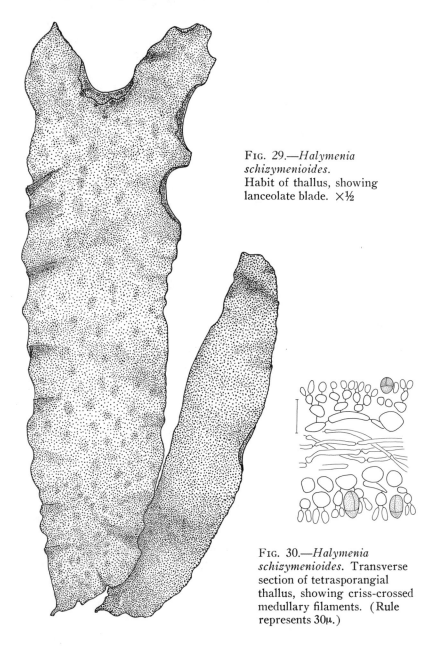

FIG. 29.—*Halymenia schizymenioides.* Habit of thallus, showing lanceolate blade. ×½

FIG. 30.—*Halymenia schizymenioides.* Transverse section of tetrasporangial thallus, showing criss-crossed medullary filaments. (Rule represents 30μ.)

Removed247 ## Lobocolax Howe, 1914

This genus has been removed from the flora; see the note follow-ing the key for Family Cryptonemiaceae, on page 67.

NA198 ## Family DERMOCORYNIDACEAE

A small family, containing only the genus *Dermocorynus*. Simi-lar to the family Cryptonemiaceae in having female reproductive structures in clusters of bushy filaments, but having the carpogonial branch associated with the auxiliary cell that is the supporting cell. In the latter character, this family resembles the Kallymeniaceae. Characters as in the genus *Dermocorynus*.

NA198 ## Dermocorynus Crouan and Crouan, 1858

Thallus consisting of an expanded crust up to 5 cm. in diameter. When fertile, sending up a few flattened or cylindrical branches on which are borne the reproductive structures. Structure of crust sometimes differentiated into hypothallus, the crust 50–170 μ thick. Erect simple branches 0.5–2 mm. tall, consisting of a filamentous medulla and a loosely compacted filamentous cortex. With pro-carps. One carpogonial branch associated with the auxiliary cell that is the supporting cell. Cystocarps without pericarps, 90–130 μ in diameter, embedded in the fertile branches. Tetrasporangia cru-ciately divided, scattered over the entire surface of the fruiting branches.

STRUCTURE AND REPRODUCTION. Hollenberg, 1940, pp. 868–77, figs. 1–6.

With a single species in the local flora.

NA198 ## Dermocorynus occidentalis Hollenberg
FIG. 31
Hollenberg, 1940, p. 868.

Plants forming thin, brownish-red, horizontally expanded thalli up to 5 cm. in diameter, and, when fertile, forming erect, simple branches less than 1 mm. tall, which bear the reproductive struc-tures.

LOCAL DISTRIBUTION. On small rocks in sand, at the −1.5-foot tide level, Middle Reef of Moss Beach.

TYPE LOCALITY. Laguna Beach, California.

PACIFIC COAST DISTRIBUTION. Pacific Grove; and from southern Cali-fornia (Los Angeles County) to Baja California (Punta Banda).

We list this species with some hesitation, for the northern plants differ somewhat from those of southern California. The erect branches are smaller and shorter, and the tetrasporangial branches are not at all flattened as are those of the southern plants. Further collections are needed.

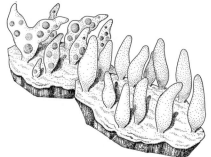

Fig. 31.—*Dermocorynus occidentalis.* Habit of fertile branches arising from the basal crust. ×15

Family KALLYMENIACEAE   NC,R248
(= CALLYMENIACEAE, Smith)

Carpogonial and auxiliary cell filaments borne in a common branched fertile filament, or borne separately. The carpogonial filaments three-celled. The auxiliary cell the supporting cell of the carpogonial filaments, or the supporting cell of another branched system bearing nonfunctional carpogonial filaments or subsidiary cells representing these filaments. Gonimoblast filaments growing toward center of blade. Cystocarps globose, fairly massive, encircled by remains of a nutritive tissue.

Description amended by the work of Norris, 1957, pp. 251–334; pls. 28–40.

REVISED KEY TO THE GENERA IN THE LOCAL FLORA   R248

1. Thalli pulvinate, parasitic........................*Callocolax* (p. 252)
1. Thalli not parasitic.. 2
  2. Thallus blade-like 3
  2. Thallus dissected into many branches (with the
    exception of *C. firma*)...............*Callophyllis* (p. 249; below)
3. With a strong midrib, blade frequently
  eroded ....*Erythrophyllum* (p. 292; below)
3. Without a midrib... 4
  4. Blades thin and soft, medulla of large cells surrounded
    by small filaments.....................*Pugetia* (p. 253; below)
  4. Blades thick and firm.. 5
5. Medulla of elongate filaments, some star-shaped....*Kallymenia* (below)
5. Medulla of large cells surrounded by
  small filaments...................*Callophyllis firma* (p. 254; below)

NA248   **Kallymenia** J. G. Agardh, 1842

Plants blade-like, simple, or divided into lobes. Structurally composed of a thin cortex of up to 5 cells in thickness, and a relatively narrow medulla of filamentous construction. On becoming mature, some to most of the filaments of the medulla become modified by radiating extensions of connections with adjacent cells and enlarge greatly, producing in some species very large stellate cells, containing dense but highly refractive substances. Tetrasporangia scattered over the thallus, cruciately divided. Cystocarps large, bulging on both sides of the thallus, with an ostiole on one or both sides. Procarps absent, the carpogonial and auxiliary cells being on separate supporting cells, the auxiliary cells bearing several sterile subsidiary cells.

STRUCTURE AND REPRODUCTION. Norris, 1957, pp. 251–334; pls. 28–40. With one species in the local flora.

NA248   **Kallymenia norrisii** Hollenberg and Abbott
FIG. 32
        Hollenberg and Abbott, 1965, p. 1183; pl. 1, fig. 3; text fig. 11.

Thalli blade-like, the blades up to 25 cm. tall and 20 cm. broad, reddish-brown in color. Blades of firm to cartilaginous texture. With a disc-shaped holdfast and a short stipe. Cortex thin, of up to 5 layers, the inner cells frequently bearing short stellate processes. Medulla, occupying $\frac{1}{3}$ to $\frac{1}{2}$ of the section, at first consisting of many branched, thin, cylindrical cells provided with many arms, the cells becoming thickened with age (stellate cells) and lying in more or less continuous sheets with arms intertwined and pointing in all directions, some of the arms establishing secondary pit connections with neighboring cells. Single arms of the cells may extend over 1 mm. in length. One carpogonium and 4–5 subsidiary cells borne on a supporting cell; auxiliary cell bearing 4–5 subsidiary cells also. Cystocarps up to 3 mm. in diameter.

LOCAL DISTRIBUTION. Dredged from depths of 5–10 fathoms on shale at south end of Monterey Bay. In 80 feet, off Pescadero Point.
TYPE LOCALITY. Dredged in 8–10 fathoms on shale at south end of Monterey Bay.
PACIFIC COAST DISTRIBUTION. As above.

R249   **Callophyllis** Kützing, 1843

Thalli erect, repeatedly branched, or blade-like and prostrate, sometimes with a peltate attachment. Vegetatively distinguished by filaments of small colored cells between the large cells of the

Fig. 32.—*Kallymenia norrisii*. Habit of thallus, showing puckering and thickening on lower portion of blade. ×⅜

medulla. Further distinguished by one (monocarpogonial) or more (polycarpogonial) carpogonial branches on the supporting cell, the supporting cell functioning as the auxiliary cell. Procarps present. Cystocarps usually very large, with one to many ostioles. Tetrasporangia embedded in the outer cortex, or sometimse modifying the surface and forming a sorus, cruciately divided.

STRUCTURE AND REPRODUCTION. Norris, 1957, pp. 251–334; pls. 28–40.

SYSTEMATICS OF WEST COAST SPECIES. Abbott and Norris, 1965, pp. 67–84; pls. 1–14.

REVISED KEY TO THE SPECIES IN THE LOCAL FLORA   R249

1. With one carpogonial branch on a supporting cell.................. 2
1. With more than one carpogonial branch on a supporting cell......... 7
   2. Thallus unbranched, with simple or dissected blades..*C. firma* (below)
   2. Thallus branched... 3

3. Thalli growing in close tufts on rocks, segments linear
   with acuminate tips..........................*C. linearis* (below)
3. Thalli in loose tufts or not tufted, usually epiphytic................. 4
   4. Thalli with main axis up to 5 times broader than
      subsequent branches.....................*C. flabellulata* (below)
   4. Thalli with main axis as broad as next order of branches......... 5
5. Ultimate segments long, linear, usually
   paired...........................*C. obtusifolia* (p. 252; below)
5. Ultimate segments short, crowded............................... 6
   6. Tips of segments broadly rounded, sometimes
      toothed...............................*C. thompsonii* (below)
   6. Tips of segments much dissected or finely
      dentate................................*C. violacea* (below)
7. Margins of branches raised, crisp, branches frequently
   furrowed..........................*C. crenulata* (p. 250; below)
7. Margins of branches smooth, branches not furrowed................ 8
   8. Thallus slippery; tetrasporangia in the angles
      of the branches........................*C. heanophylla* (below)
   8. Thallus firm, coarse; tetrasporangia scattered throughout
      the thallus..........................*C. pinnata* (p. 251; below)

Monocarpogonial Species

Callophyllis flabellulata Harvey

Harvey, 1862, p. 171. Kylin, 1925; p. 34, figs. 15–16. Doty, 1947, p. 174. Abbott and Norris, 1965, p. 70; pl. 2, figs. 1–2; pl. 3, figs. 1–2.
Callophyllis marginifructa Setchell and Swezy *in* Setchell, 1923, p. 398. Smith, 1944, p. 250; pl. 58, figs. 3–4 (including synonymy).
Callophyllis acrocarpa Setchell, 1923, p. 398.
Callophyllis filicina Setchell and Swezy *in* Setchell, 1923, p. 398.
Callophyllis gardneri Setchell, 1923, p. 399.
Callophyllis odonthalioides Setchell, 1923, p. 399.
Callophyllis crassifolia Setchell and Swezy *in* Setchell, 1923A, p. 398. Smith, 1944, p. 250.

Thalli 4–10(3–18) cm. high, those less than 5 cm. usually of subtidal occurrence, orange-red to dark red, some of them drying black. Thalli usually in rounded tufts, saxicolous or growing on worm tubes, rarely epiphytic. Main axis up to 5 times as broad as subsequent branches, the 5–6 orders of branches becoming thinner and more finely divided as well as shorter, the ultimate branches 1 mm. or less to 1 cm. or more wide. Cystocarps umbonate or beaked, with one or more ostioles, located on the margin or within it, or on the faces of the lobes, or in both places.

LOCAL DISTRIBUTION. Dredged from depths of 6–12 fathoms, on worm tubes and in sandy mud, on shale at south end of Monterey Bay. Between the mean and −1.5-foot tide levels, at Mussel Point; Point Pinos; Moss Beach; Point Joe; Pescadero Point; Pebble Beach; Mission Point; and near the mouth of Little Sur River. Also frequently found subtidally and in the Carmel Submarine Canyon to depths of 125 feet.

TYPE LOCALITY. Esquimalt Harbor, Vancouver Island.

PACIFIC COAST DISTRIBUTION. British Columbia to Baja California.

Callophyllis linearis (Kylin) Abbott and Norris NC,R268

Abbott and Norris, 1965, p. 72; pl. 4, fig. 1.
Basonym: *Gracilaria linearis* Kylin, 1941, p. 22; pl. 7, fig. 19. Smith, 1944, p. 268; pl. 63, fig. 3. Dawson, 1949, p. 38; pl. 20, figs. 7–10.

Thalli 2–8 cm. tall, purplish-brown in color. Saxicolous, closely tufted, unequally dichotomously branched to the third or fourth order, canaliculate, crisp in texture, tips acuminate, or dentate, or bifurcate. Tetrasporangia in irregular sori, occasionally spread beyond the sori. Spermatangia in small irregular sori near the tips of the plants. Cystocarps few, up to 1 mm. in diameter, projecting but inconspicuous, borne on both surfaces of the segments, some near the margin.

LOCAL DISTRIBUTION. On exposed headlands, at the −1.0- to −1.5-foot tide levels, at Point Pinos; Pescadero Point; Punta de los Lobos marinas; rocks north of Malpaso Creek; near Little Sur River; and 10 miles south of Point Sur.

TYPE LOCALITY. Point Pinos, Pacific Grove.

PACIFIC COAST DISTRIBUTION. As above, and dredged from a depth of 25 feet, off Punta Banda, Baja California.

Callophyllis firma (Kylin) Norris NC254

Norris, 1957, p. 287; figs. 13–19. Abbott and Norris, 1965, p. 74.
Pugetia firma Kylin, 1941, p. 15; pl. 4, fig. 12. Smith, 1944, p. 254; pl. 60, fig. 1.

Norris' study of this species showed that the development of the female reproductive structures is more like *Callophyllis* than *Pugetia*, even though the form of the foliose thalli has more in common with *Pugetia* as exemplified by the type species, *P. fragilissima* Kylin.

LOCAL DISTRIBUTION (additional). Subtidally, to a depth of 100 feet, at Pescadero Point; Arrowhead Point.

PACIFIC COAST DISTRIBUTION. Northern British Columbia to central California (Monterey Peninsula); subtidally at 80 feet, off Santa Cruz Island; at 100 feet, off Anacapa Island; at 40 feet, off Imperial Beach, San Diego County; and subtidally at 80 feet, off Punta Santo Tomas, Baja California.

The subtidal plants are tough and slippery; the intertidal specimens are crisp.

NC,R251 **Callophyllis violacea** J. G. Agardh

> J. G. Agardh, 1885, p. 34. Abbott and Norris, 1965, p. 74; pl. 4, fig. 2; pl. 5,
> figs. 1–2; pl. 6, figs. 1–2.
> *Callophyllis gracilarioides* Anderson, 1891, p. 223.
> *Callophyllis megalocarpa* Setchell and Swezy *in* Setchell, 1923*A*, p. 401.
> Smith, 1944, p. 251; pl. 59, fig. 1. Dawson, 1954, p. 295; pl. 5, fig. 46; pl. 34, fig. 81.
> *Callophyllis plumosa* Setchell and Swezy *in* Setchell, 1923, p. 400.
> *Callophyllis dissecta* Setchell and Swezy *in* Setchell, 1923, p. 401.
> *Callophyllis violacea* var. *epiphytica* Dawson, 1954, p. 401; pl. 5, fig. 44; pl. 43,
> fig. 91.

Thalli 5–27 cm. high (average 15 cm.), dark red to purplish-red in color. Usually epiphytic, with one to several branches from a disc-shaped holdfast, fleshy to cartilaginous, sometimes furrowed. If epiphytic, generally fan-shaped; if saxicolous, then tufted. Main axis 1–4 cm. wide at the base, branching near the base and expanding before branching again. Branches usually alternate to the fifth or sixth order, the upper segments shorter and more crowded. Tips toothed on a broadly rounded or spatulate apex, or much dissected. Tetrasporangia scattered. Cystocarps up to 3 mm. in diameter, scattered, projecting prominently especially when old.

LOCAL DISTRIBUTION. Frequently dredged from depths of 8–10 fathoms on sandy mud, at south end of Monterey Bay. Between the 1.5- and −1.5-foot tide levels, at Point Pinos; Asilomar Point; Fanshell Beach; Pebble Beach; Mission Point; and exposed headlands south to the mouth of Little Sur River. Also cast ashore at Point Pinos; south end of Carmel Beach.

TYPE LOCALITY. Santa Barbara, California.

PACIFIC COAST DISTRIBUTION. British Columbia to Baja California.

This is one of the three most commonly occurring species of *Callophyllis* on the Pacific Coast, the other two being *C. flabellulata* and *C. pinnata*. *C. violacea* is more common and more variable south of Santa Barbara than it is north of Point Conception.

R252 **Callophyllis obtusifolia** J. G. Agardh

> J. G. Agardh, 1851, p. 297. Smith, 1944, p. 252; pl. 59, fig. 2. Dawson, 1954,
> p. 296; pl. 35, fig. 82; pl. 36, fig. 83. Abbott and Norris, 1965, p. 75; pl. 7, fig. 2;
> pl. 8, figs. 1–2.
> *Callophyllis phyllohaptera* Dawson, 1954, p. 298; pl. 39, fig. 86.

Thalli 15–50 cm. tall, deep red to dark brown, mostly epiphytic, usually pinnately and rarely palmately branched, proliferous late in the season, also regenerative at that time. With long, linear, usually paired segments, the terminal dichotomy 6–18 cm. long, the tips usually obtuse or bifurcate. Tetrasporangia scattered over the thallus, sometimes germinating in place and giving the thallus a papillate aspect. Cystocarps scattered, usually less than 1 mm. in diameter but some 1.5 mm. wide.

LOCAL DISTRIBUTION. Middle Reef of Moss Beach; west of Fanshell Beach; Mission Point. Also cast ashore at Moss Beach.

TYPE LOCALITY. Presumably the Monterey Peninsula (a collection by Haenke).

PACIFIC COAST DISTRIBUTION. Central California (Bolinas, Marin County) to Baja California (Punta Entrada, Isla Magdalena).

This infrequently occurring species is most easily confused with *C. pinnata,* from which it can be distinguished vegetatively by having terminal dichotomies longer than its penultimate dichotomies. The relationship is reversed in *C. pinnata.* The most reliable criterion for this species is monocarpogony.

Callophyllis thompsonii Setchell   NA249

Setchell, 1923, p. 399. Abbott and Norris, 1965, p. 76; pl. 9, fig. 1.   FIG. 33

Thalli 8–12(20) cm. tall, dark purple-red in color. Branches arising from a small disc, 3–5 times dichotomously flabellate, ultimate lobes broadly rounded, 1.5–2 cm. wide, with a few broad teeth. Cystocarps strictly seriate within the margin. Tetrasporangia scattered in the upper parts of the thallus.

LOCAL DISTRIBUTION. Dredged from 8–10 fathoms, off a sandy, muddy bottom, in several locations off Monterey, at south end of Monterey Bay.

TYPE LOCALITY. Dredged off Canoe Island, Washington.

PACIFIC COAST DISTRIBUTION. As above, and off Whidbey Island, Washington.

Resembling stubby forms of *C. violacea,* but with broader tips; otherwise resembling *C. crenulata,* which is polycarpogonial.

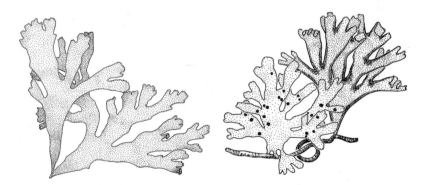

FIG. 33 (*left*)—*Callophyllis thompsonii.* Habit of plant, showing broad penultimate segments characteristic of the species. ×⅜

FIG. 34 (*right*) — *Callophyllis heanophylla.* Habit of thalli growing on worm tubes at several fathoms' depth: left, cystocarpic thallus; right, tetrasporangial thallus. ×1⅓

Polycarpogonial Species

R250 **Callophyllis crenulata** Setchell

Setchell, 1923*A*, p. 400. Smith, 1944, p. 250; pl. 58, fig. 1. Abbott and Norris, 1965, p. 77; pl. 9, fig. 2; pl. 10, figs. 1–2.

Thalli 7–14(3–20) cm. tall, orange-red to dark purplish-red, drying to dull rose in color. Saxicolous or epiphytic, of a single or few erect, sometimes canaliculate, branches. Branching flabellate, rarely proliferous. Penultimate segments broadest, up to 2 cm. wide. Ultimate segments, if 3–5 cm. wide, with irregular teeth; if 1–2 cm. wide, tips somewhat spathulate with crenulated margins. Margins of all thalli smooth, undulate to crenulate but at all times crisp and somewhat raised. Spermatangia in light-colored terminal patches; tetrasporangia scattered; cystocarps scattered, 1–3 mm. in diameter, flat, sometimes beaked, with 1–3 ostioles.

LOCAL DISTRIBUTION. At the −1.0- to −1.5-foot tide levels, at Pescadero Point; Mission Point; near Malpaso Creek; and near the mouth of Little Sur River. Frequently found cast ashore near all rocky headlands: Mussel Point; Point Pinos; Asilomar Point; Moss Beach; Mission Point.

TYPE LOCALITY. Whidbey Island, Washington.

PACIFIC COAST DISTRIBUTION. British Columbia (Vancouver Island) to Central California (Little Sur River).

Proliferous specimens, like the type specimen, appear to be common in relatively calm areas like Puget Sound. Only narrowly branched specimens with no proliferations, and with strongly crispate margins, are found on the Monterey Peninsula.

NA249 **Callophyllis heanophylla** Setchell
FIG. 34

Setchell, 1923, p. 401. Norris, 1957, p. 281; text figs. 9–10; pl. 36. Abbott and Norris, 1965, p. 79; pl. 11, fig. 2.

Thalli up to 7 cm. tall, mostly shorter, often growing on annelid or bryozoan tubes, dark rose-red in color, slippery and soft. With short stipes soon giving rise to dichotomously flabellate blades of three orders. Segments scarcely more than 2 cm. at the widest, tips obtuse to irregularly rounded, sometimes a little dentate. Tetrasporangia restricted to the angles of penultimate and ultimate dichotomies, in slightly modified submarginal sori. Cystocarps 0.5 to 0.75 mm. in diameter, distributed irregularly in the upper branches, bulging on both sides of the thallus, with small ostioles.

LOCAL DISTRIBUTION. Dredged frequently from depths of 6–10 fathoms, on worm tubes and arborescent bryozoans, near the Municipal Wharf, Monterey Harbor.

TYPE LOCALITY. Canoe Island, Washington.

PACIFIC COAST DISTRIBUTION. Northern Washington, Oregon, and the Monterey Peninsula.

The Monterey plants are smaller than those from Washington, but agree in all other respects.

Callophyllis pinnata Setchell and Swezy   R251

Setchell and Swezy *in* Setchell, 1923*A*, p. 400. Smith, 1944, p. 251; pl. 58, fig. 2. Dawson, 1954, p. 299; pl. 5, fig. 41; pl. 40, fig. 87. Abbott and Norris, 1965, p. 80; pl. 12, figs. 1–2; pl. 13, figs. 1–2.

Thalli up to 45 cm. tall, mostly 12–30 cm., deep rose to deep red to almost black in color. Usually epiphytic on *Botryoglossum.* Coarse in texture. Cystocarpic specimens differing in shape from tetrasporangial specimens. Cystocarpic specimens mostly pal- mately-flabellately divided, with main segments 2–3 cm. wide and 10–30 cm. long from the main dichotomies, branching to the fourth or fifth orders, tips straight on somewhat pointed ultimate seg- ments, or tips dissected on broad to pointed ultimate segments. Tetrasporangial plants more loosely and irregularly branched, the main segments usually not more than 2 cm. wide, 15–45 cm. long at the main dichotomies, branching to the third or fourth orders, tips mostly straight and gradually pointed, rarely dissected. Mar- gins of older plants sometimes with proliferations less than 1 cm. up to 8 cm. long, less than 1.0 up to 1.5 cm. wide, distichously placed along main margins but rarely on margins of branches of higher orders. Tetrasporangia scattered over the blade, the tetra- spores frequently germinating there and forming small, rough papillae. Cystocarps scattered over the blades, less than 2 mm. in diameter.

LOCAL DISTRIBUTION (additional). Between the 1.0- and −1.0-foot tide levels, at all rocky headlands: Mussel Point; Point Pinos; Asilomar Point; Moss Beach; Mission Point.

PACIFIC COAST DISTRIBUTION. Washington to Baja California.

Next to *C. flabellulata,* this is the most common species in cen- tral California.

Pugetia Kylin, 1925   R253

Having the same internal vegetative structure as *Callophyllis,* i.e., large medullary cells interspersed by small photosynthetic fila- ments, but having the auxiliary cell separated from the carpogonial branches (borne on separate supporting cells), a connecting fila- ment necessary for the transfer of the diploid nucleus. All species known are blade-like.

STRUCTURE AND REPRODUCTION. Norris, 1957, pp. 266–76, figs. 3–6.

With one species in the local flora. [*Pugetia firma* Kylin (p. 254, Smith) has been transferred to *Callophyllis* as *C. firma* (Kylin) Norris.]

NA254
FIG. 35

Pugetia fragilissima Kylin

Kylin, 1925, p 31, fig. 14. Norris, 1957, p. 266; text figs. 3–5; pls. 29–30.

Thalli membranous, up to 15 cm. in diameter, circular in outline to cleft, the margins entire and sometimes fimbriate. Rose-red in color. Cystocarps up to 1 mm. in diameter, mostly smaller, densely crowding the surface of the blades and giving the thallus the texture of fine sandpaper.

LOCAL DISTRIBUTION. Dredged from depths of 6–10 fathoms, usually attached to worm tubes but occasionally on small pebbles, near the Municipal Wharf, Monterey Harbor. Cast ashore at Pacific Grove. Rarely cast ashore in Monterey Harbor and at Mussel Point.

TYPE LOCALITY. Canoe Island, Washington.

PACIFIC COAST DISTRIBUTION. British Columbia; Washington; and the Monterey Peninsula.

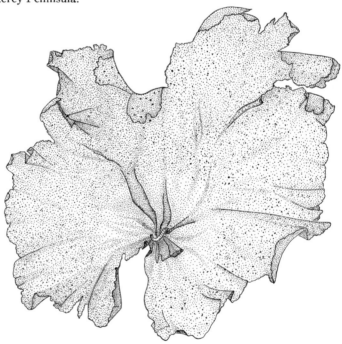

FIG. 35.—*Pugetia fragilissima.* Habit of thallus growing on worm tubes, taken from several fathoms' depth in Monterey Harbor. ×½

Erythrophyllum delesserioides J. G. Agardh

Transfer292

This species (and genus) has been transferred by Norris (1957, p. 298) to the Kallymeniaceae (with no other change in status) from Order Gigartinales, Family Gigartinaceae, because of the similarity of female reproductive structures. It appears to be most clearly related, on this basis, to *Pugetia*.

Order GIGARTINALES

Revised Key to the Families in the Local Flora

R256

1. The auxiliary cell a modified vegetative cell some distance
    from the carpogonial filament.................................. 2
1. The auxiliary cell either the supporting cell of a carpogonial
    filament or the cell immediately below.......................... 4
    2. Gonimoblast arising from the connecting
        filament ....Cruoriaceae (p. 216)
    2. Gonimoblast arising from an auxiliary cell..................... 3
3. Gonimoblast filaments growing toward thallus
    surface ....Nemastomaceae (p. 256)
3. Gonimoblast filaments growing (at least at first)
    toward interior of thallus...............Solieriaceae (p. 259; below)
    4. The supporting cell without sterile filaments.................... 5
    4. The supporting cell with sterile filaments....................... 6
5. Gonimoblast filaments growing toward interior of thallus;
    tetrasporangia at thallus surface.......Plocamiaceae (p. 262; below)
5. Gonimoblast filaments growing toward thallus center; tetra-
    sporangia in masses deep within thallus. Gigartinaceae (p. 276; below)
    6. The auxiliary cell not fusing with adjacent cells;
        tetrasporangia in nemathecia.....Phyllophoraceae (p. 269; below)
    6. The auxiliary cell fusing with adjacent cells; tetrasporangia
        separated from one another........Gracilariaceae (p. 265; below)

Family SOLIERIACEAE

Revised Key to the Genera in the Local Flora

R259

1. Thalli not parasitic.. 2
1. Thalli parasitic..............................*Gardneriella* (p. 261)
    2. Thalli cylindrical, radially branched.....*Agardhiella* (p. 259; below)
    2. Thalli not cylindrical....................................... 3
3. Thalli regularly dichotomously branched, flattened and compressed
    with tips very acutely pointed..................*Sarcodiotheca* (below)
3. Thalli expanded blades, each from a stout stipe, with more blades
    or rounded proliferations from the margin........*Opuntiella* (p. 261)

Agardhiella tenera (J. G. Agardh) Schmitz

NC260

Schmitz, 1889, p. 441. Dawson, 1961A, p. 231 (including synonymy).
Rhabdonia tenera J. G. Agardh, 1852, p. 354.
Agardhiella coulteri (Harvey) Setchell, *in* Phyc. Bor.-Amer. No. 333. Smith, 1944, p. 260; pl. 62, fig. 4 (including synonymy).

PACIFIC COAST DISTRIBUTION. British Columbia to Mexico (Revilla Gigedo Archipelago).

The uniting of the two species, one previously known from the East Coast of North America (*A. tenera*), and the other from the West Coast (*A. coulteri*) appears to be correct. In our own area, we have noticed that plants of the higher intertidal (2.0- to 1.0-foot tide levels) are the coarse, thick form most commonly collected, whereas those from the —1.5-foot tide level to 40 feet subtidally are as small as ¼ the diameter of the intertidal ones, and more wiry. A study of the external vegetative features, including branching and internal structure, and a study of the reproductive structures, show no difference between the plants from the two very different habitats, or at best that there is an intergrading series. This conclusion can also be reached when examining a large series of specimens from both coasts.

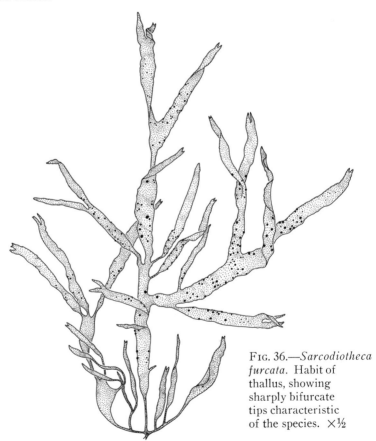

FIG. 36.—*Sarcodiotheca furcata.* Habit of thallus, showing sharply bifurcate tips characteristic of the species. ×½

Sarcodiotheca Kylin, 1932 NA259

Thalli erect, up to 25 cm. tall. Regularly or irregularly dichotomously branched, the branches flattened. Outer cortex of 2–3 layers of small cells; inner cortex of very large cells, appearing parenchymatous. Medulla of densely packed thin filaments. Cystocarps projecting, with a pericarp. Spermatangia in minutely mottled sori. Tetrasporangia zonately divided, scattered over the thallus.

STRUCTURE AND REPRODUCTION. Kylin, 1932, p. 16.

With one species in the local flora.

Sarcodiotheca furcata (Setchell and Gardner) Kylin NA259 FIG. 36

Kylin, 1932, p. 16. Dawson, 1961*A*, p. 229; pl. 30, figs. 1–2; pl. 31, figs. 1, 4.
Anatheca furcata Setchell and Gardner, 1903, p. 310; pl. 23, fig. 39; pl. 24, fig. 41.

Blades from 1.0 to 2.5 cm. broad, repeatedly branched. Tips very sharply bifurcate, the furcations of equal length.

LOCAL DISTRIBUTION. Dredged from a depth of 8 fathoms, on shale at south end of Monterey Bay.

TYPE LOCALITY. West coast of Whidbey Island, Washington.

PACIFIC COAST DISTRIBUTION. Discontinuously and subtidally from northern British Columbia to the Galapagos Archipelago.

Family PLOCAMIACEAE 262

Plocamium coccineum var. pacificum (Kylin) Dawson NC264

Dawson, 1961*A*, p. 264.
Plocamium pacificum Kylin, 1925, p. 42; fig. 24*b*. Smith, 1944, p. 264; pl. 62, fig. 1 (including synonymy).

LOCAL DISTRIBUTION (additional). Collected subtidally at 125 feet in the Monterey Submarine Canyon, and therefore one of the deepest growing red algae known in our range.

Dawson correctly points out that there is a wide range in variation among the characters selected by Kylin to separate *P. pacificum* from *P. coccineum*. We therefore agree with him that the Pacific Coast plants, distinguished by their robust nature from the European specimens, should have at most varietal rank.

Family GRACILARIACEAE

REVISED KEY TO THE GENERA IN THE LOCAL FLORA R266

1. Thalli parasitic.............................*Gracilariophila* (p. 268)
1. Thalli free-living 2

2. With connecting filaments between pericarp and
   gonimoblast . . . .*Gracilaria* (p. 266; below)
2. Without connecting filaments between pericarp and
   gonimoblast . . . .*Gracilariopsis* (below)

NC,R266, 267

Gracilariopsis Dawson, 1949

Vegetative and reproductive structures similar to that for *Graci-laria,* as described in Smith. The cystocarps of *Gracilariopsis,* how-ever, lack connecting filaments between the gonimoblast and the pericarp.

R266, 267

KEY TO THE SPECIES IN THE LOCAL FLORA

1. Thalli over 15 cm. long, filiform, irregularly
   branched. . . . .*G. sjoestedtii* (p. 267; below)
1. Thalli less than 10 cm. long, stout, with few
   dichotomies. . . . .*G. robusta* (p. 267; below)

NC,R267   ## Gracilariopsis sjoestedtii (Kylin) Dawson

Dawson, 1949, p. 40.
Gracilaria sjoestedtii Kylin, 1930, p. 55. Smith, 1944, p. 267; pl. 63, fig. 4.

Dawson segregated from the genus *Gracilaria* those species showing lack of connecting filaments between the gonimoblast and the pericarp, forming a new genus, *Gracilariopsis,* and retaining those species showing connecting filaments in *Gracilaria.* This dis-tinction has been found to be clear in this species and in *Graci-lariopsis robusta,* and should be a welcome aid to identification of species in this highly polymorphic complex.

NC267   ## Gracilariopsis robusta (Setchell) Dawson

Dawson, 1949, p. 42.
Gracilaria robusta Setchell, *in* Phyc. Bor.-Amer. No. 635. Smith, 1944, p. 267; pl. 63, fig. 2 (including synonymy).
LOCAL DISTRIBUTION (additional). Between the 1.0- and −1.5-foot tide levels in the region of the type locality. Subtidally at 25 feet, Mussel Point.

A relatively rare species, but not uncommon in the type locality.

R266   # Gracilaria Greville, 1830

Connecting filaments between the gonimoblast and the pericarp present. Otherwise, as described in Smith.

STRUCTURE AND REPRODUCTION. Dawson, 1949, pp. 3–39.

With one species in the local flora. [*Gracilaria linearis* Kylin has been transferred to *Callophyllis* (Order Cryptonemiales, Family Kallymeniaceae) as *C. linearis* (Kylin) Abbott and Norris.]

Gracilaria verrucosa (Hudson) Papenfuss

Papenfuss, 1950, p. 195. Dawson, 1961A, p. 214; pl. 20.
Gracilaria confervoides (Linnaeus) Greville. Dawson, 1949, p. 13; pl. 15, fig. 9.

NA266
FIG. 37

Thalli 30 cm. tall, or more, yellowish at the tips, brownish-purple below in color. With several leading cylindrical axes from a small conical holdfast, the axes branched sparingly and usually radially, the main axes beset from the base to midway to the apex with simple or branched spines. The upper portions of the branches densely crowded with colorless hairs up to 1 mm. in length, these becoming deciduous. Tetrasporangia scattered over the thallus. Cystocarps not prominent, hemispherical to rounded. Connecting filaments present in the cystocarp.

LOCAL DISTRIBUTION. Growing in coarse sand between the 1.5- and 0.5-foot tide levels, at Mussel Point; Asilomar Point; Pebble Beach.

TYPE LOCALITY. England.

PACIFIC COAST DISTRIBUTION. Discontinuous, from southern British Columbia to Pacific Mexico and the Gulf of California.

This species resembles *Gracilariopsis sjoestedtii* (*Gracilaria sjoestedtii* in Smith) and finely branched specimens of *Agardhiella tenera* (*A. coulteri,* in Smith), and has probably been passed over because of this.

Family PHYLLOPHORACEAE

REVISED KEY TO THE GENERA IN THE LOCAL FLORA   R269

1. Thalli with cylindrical branches............*Ahnfeltia* (p. 271; below)
1. Thalli with all or the ends of branches flattened...................2
  2. Compressed or partly flattened except
     at base...............................*Gymnogongrus* (p. 272)
  2. Flattened throughout, with ribbon-like segments................3
3. Cystocarps in long linear nemathecia, appearing
   vein-like.........................*Stenogramme* (p. 275; below)
3. Cystocarps not in linear nemathecia............................4
  4. With spermatangia in cavities...............*Phyllophora* (p. 269)
  4. With spermatangia in elevated surface
     patches................................*Petroglossum* (below)

Petroglossum Hollenberg, 1943   NA269

Thalli saxicolous, branches several to numerous and erect from an expanded crustose base, leaf-like, simple to irregularly dichotomously flabellate, commonly stipitate. Branches relatively narrow, flattened, with few to many lateral proliferations, or lacking proliferations. Texture firm and cartilaginous. Medulla of large thick-

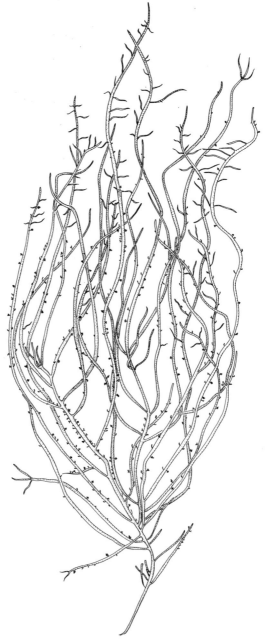

FIG. 37.—*Gracilaria verrucosa*. Habit of thallus, showing spines on upper branches characteristic of specimens taken from Pebble Beach. ×½

walled cells and cortex of mostly 1–2 layers of small cells. Tetrasporangia cruciately divided, in catenate anticlinal rows of 3–5, aggregated in nemathecioid sori which bulge on both surfaces of the ultimate branches. Cystocarps mostly borne singly in the center toward the narrowed base of the thallus divisions, or in larger plants mostly in lateral proliferations, bulging on both sides of the branches, without an ostiole. Spermatangial sori forming rounded and slightly elevated surface patches in the center or mostly toward the tips of the branches.

STRUCTURE AND REPRODUCTION. Hollenberg, 1943, pp. 571–73, figs. 1–6.

With one species in the local flora.

Petroglossum parvum Hollenberg

NA269
FIG. 38

Hollenberg, 1945, p. 450.

Plants up to 5 cm. tall, most often less, with a few simple, erect branches arising from a rhizomatous base, with few or no lateral proliferations near the base, of a brownish-red color. Blades may remain simple and lanceolate, or may appear wider at the top, forking once. With the exception of one spermatangial specimen, plants from this area attributed to this species are sterile.

LOCAL DISTRIBUTION. Growing in low tufts on vertical faces of rocks, at about the −1.0-foot tide level: Mission Point; near the mouth of Little Sur River. Also cast ashore at Pebble Beach.

TYPE LOCALITY. Laguna Beach, California.

PACIFIC COAST DISTRIBUTION. Monterey region; and from southern California (Laguna Beach) to Baja California (Isla Cedros).

If fertile, spermatangial plants would differ from those of *Phyllophora* in having sori that are nearly flush with the surface. *Petroglossum* differs from a young *Rhodymenia*, which it resembles, by the proliferations, if any proliferations are present, and by a thicker cortical layer.

Ahnfeltia gigartinoides J. G. Agardh

NI272

This species has been placed in synonymy with *A. concinna* J. G. Agardh by Dawson (1961, p. 245). We do not accept this transfer at this time because of the fact that *A. concinna,* whose type locality is the Hawaiian Islands, has a very different vegetative structure from those going under the name *A. gigartinoides* on the Pacific Coast.

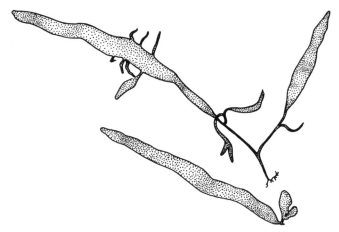

FIG. 38.—*Petroglossum parvum*. Habit of sterile thalli. ×1½

NC276 **Stenogramme interrupta** (C. A. Agardh) Montagne

> Montagne, 1846, p. 483. Taylor, 1945, p. 241. Dawson, 1961*A*, p. 253.
> *Delesseria interrupta* C. A. Agardh, 1822, p. 179.
> *Stenogramme californica* Harvey, 1841, p. 408. Smith, 1944, p. 276; pl. 64, fig. 4; pl. 65, fig. 4.

> LOCAL DISTRIBUTION (additional). In large clusters in areas where sand frequently scours rock surfaces at the 1.0- to −1.0-foot tide levels. Also from a depth of 40 feet in the Carmel Submarine Canyon, on sand; and dredged from depths of 8–10 fathoms on sandy, muddy bottoms near Monterey Harbor.

Although most of the plants found on the West Coast are considerably wider in the blade (up to 1 cm. wide) and as tall as 22 cm., and therefore much taller than the European specimens, we believe with Taylor and others that there is not much else to distinguish this species from the European species.

276   Family GIGARTINACEAE

NI277   **Gigartina** Stackhouse, 1809

Dawson (1961*A*) made a considerable number of changes in the systematics of *Gigartina*, most of which we are not yet in a position to evaluate. We wish to indicate here only that more ecological and morphological work must be done in this area before we can offer a reasoned opinion.

Iridaea Bory, 1826 (nomen conservandum)   NC287
(= **Iridophycus** Setchell and Gardner, 1937)

Iridaea flaccida (Setchell and Gardner) Hollenberg and Abbott,   NC288
comb. nov.

Iridophycus flaccidum Setchell and Gardner, Proc. Nat. Acad. Sci., *23*: 171,
1937. Smith, 1944, p. 288; pl. 72, fig. 2 (excluding synonymy).

Although *Iridaea agardhiana* (Setchell and Gardner) Kylin
(1941, p. 23) (= *Iridophycus agardhiana* Setchell and Gardner, a
new name for *Iridaea minor* J. G. Agardh, 1849, not *Iridaea minor*
of Endlicher, 1843) appears to have been accepted by Smith (1944,
pp. 288–89) as conspecific with *Iridophycus flaccidum,* we do not
at this time accept this to be correct. The type specimen of *Iridaea
minor* J. G. Agardh is figured by Kylin (1941, pl. 8, fig. 21), and
although Smith (p. 289) believed that this specimen represents
"nothing more than a juvenile specimen of *I. flaccidum,*" we believe that because of the long stipes shown, and because Kylin
(1941, p. 23) states that the thallis is *"massig dick aber knorpelig,"*
this specimen represents *Iridaea splendens* (Setchell and Gardner)
Papenfuss. Neither of these characteristics is representative of *I.
flaccida.* Furthermore, Setchell and Gardner (1937, p. 173), in
their key to the species of the northern hemisphere, characterize
I. agardhianum as "fronds chiefly narrow in proportion to length,
often branched and with marginal pinnules on the apophysis and
blade." These are characteristics of *I. splendens* as we have observed it over many years' work in the field. Agardh's type specimen needs re-examination.

Iridaea splendens (Setchell and Gardner) Papenfuss   NC289

Papenfuss, 1958, p. 106.
Iridophycus splendens Setchell and Gardner, 1937, p. 170. Smith, 1944, p. 289;
pl. 72, fig. 1.

See also comments under *I. flaccida,* above, and under *I. sanguinea,* below.

Iridaea sanguinea (Setchell and Gardner) Hollenberg and Abbott   NC,R289

Hollenberg and Abbott, 1965, p. 1184.
Iridophycus sanguineum Setchell and Gardner, 1937, p. 172. (Not of Smith,
1944, p. 289.)

We have examined the type specimen of this species and believe that it represents a species not present on the Monterey Penin-

sula. The specimens from this area attributed by Smith to this species are *Iridaea splendens,* representing the ecological variant common to exposed headlands and showing a well-defined stipe (rare in specimens growing submerged) and a dark, blood-red color rather than the deep purple usually associated with submerged *I. splendens.* We exclude *I. sanguineum* from the local flora.

NC290 **Iridaea coriacea** (Setchell and Gardner) Scagel

Scagel, 1957, p. 190.
Iridophycus coriaceum Setchell and Gardner, 1937, p. 170. Smith, 1944, p. 290; pl. 71, fig. 4.

NC290 **Iridaea lineare** (Setchell and Gardner) Kylin

Kylin, 1941, p. 23.
Iridophycus lineare Setchell and Gardner, 1937, p. 171. Smith, 1944, p. 290; pl. 72, fig. 3.

NC291 **Iridaea heterocarpum** Postels and Ruprecht

Postels and Ruprecht, 1840, p. 18.
Iridophycus heterocarpum (Postels and Ruprecht) Setchell and Gardner, 1937, p. 170. Smith, 1944, p. 291; pl. 73, fig. 3.

Transfer292 **Erythrophyllum delesserioides** J. G. Agardh

This species (and genus) has been transferred, with no change in status, to Order Cryptonemiales, Family Kallymeniaceae (which see).

293 ## Order RHODYMENIALES

Family RHODYMENIACEAE

R294 REVISED KEY TO THE GENERA IN THE LOCAL FLORA

1. Thalli free-living 3
1. Thalli parasitic 2
  2. On *Fauchea* ....*Faucheocolax* (p. 296)
  2. On *Rhodymenia* ....*Rhodymeniocolax* (below)
3. Forming peltate blades on a stout stipe.............*Maripelta* (below)
3. Not forming peltate blades................................... 4
  4. Thallus wholly or partly saccate............................. 5
  4. Thallus flattened, with divided blades........................ 6
5. Thallus usually unbranched, but may be proliferously
    branched...............................*Halosaccion* (p. 297)
5. Thallus a branched cylinder, and each branch tip a
    hollow sac...............................*Botryocladia* (p. 296)
  6. Usually dichotomously branched; cystocarps globose
      without ornamentation 7
  6. Usually irregularly branched; cystocarps usually
      ornamented with spines................*Fauchea* (p. 295; below)

7. Thallus with conspicuous arching diaphragms........*Fryeella* (below)
7. Thallus without diaphragms, usually with prominent
    creeping rhizomes...................*Rhodymenia* (p. 298; below)

Fauchea Montagne, 1846

REVISED KEY TO THE SPECIES IN THE LOCAL FLORA   R295

1. With cystocarps scattered on the surface and
    margins of the blades.........................*F. laciniata* (below)
1. With cystocarps on the margins of the blades...................... 2
    2. Thalli up to 34 cm. tall, with segments up to
       2 cm. broad...............................*F. fryeana* (below)
    2. Thalli less than 8 cm. tall, the widest segments less
       than 1 cm. broad....................*F. galapagensis* (below)

Fauchea fryeana Setchell

NA295
FIG. 39

Setchell, 1912, p. 239; pl. 31.

Thalli up to 34 cm. tall, straw-colored to light rose in color, drying to a soft rose color. Cystocarps marginal only, closely set, and giving the margin a fimbriate appearance. Less than 10 per cent of the cystocarps are coronate, or bearing papillae or spines on the pericarps.

LOCAL DISTRIBUTION. Cast ashore at south end of Carmel Beach.
TYPE LOCALITY. Friday Harbor, Washington.
PACIFIC COAST DISTRIBUTION. Washington and the Monterey Peninsula.

Fauchea galapagensis Taylor

NA295
FIG. 40

Taylor, 1945, p. 246; pl. 82, figs. 1–2.

Thalli 5–8 cm. tall, in small rounded tufts, more or less regularly dichotomously divided, brownish-red to deep red in color. Branches 3–4 times divided, the penultimate branches up to 1 cm. wide, the ultimate segments up to 5 mm. in diameter. Tetrasporangia in mottled sori on the faces of the blades, covering the entire surfaces except those of the ultimate branches. Cystocarps 1 mm. in diameter, marginal, sometimes occurring closely together so as to produce a fimbriate margin. Not all of the cystocarps have coronate pericarps.

LOCAL DISTRIBUTION. Dredged from depths of 4–8 fathoms, on worm tubes, in Monterey Harbor; and from depths of 8–10 fathoms, on shale at south end of Monterey Bay.
TYPE LOCALITY. Isla Santa Maria, Galapagos Archipelago.
PACIFIC COAST DISTRIBUTION. As above.

Smaller and more regularly branched than *F. fryeana.*

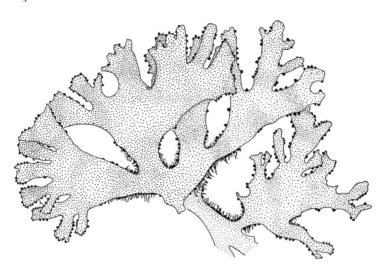

FIG. 39.—*Fauchea fryeana.* Habit of thallus, showing
marginal cystocarps. ×⁹⁄₁₀

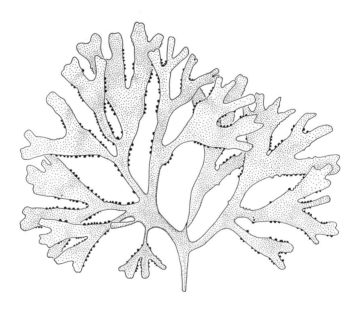

FIG. 40.—*Fauchea galapagensis.* Habit of thallus,
showing marginal cystocarps. ×1⅓

Fauchea laciniata J. G. Agardh NC,R295

J. G. Agardh, 1885, p. 40. Doty, 1947*A*, p. 185. Sparling, 1957, p. 340.
Fauchea media Kylin, 1941, p. 27; pl. 10, fig. 24. Smith, 1944, p. 295; pl. 73, fig. 1.
Fauchea laciniata f. *pygmaea* Setchell, 1912, p. 238. Dawson, 1963, p. 440.

LOCAL DISTRIBUTION (additional). West of the Coast Guard pier, Monterey Harbor; on the sides of a sardine hopper near the canneries, Monterey; near the mouth of Little Sur River. Also dredged from a depth of 6 fathoms, on shale at south end of Monterey Bay.
TYPE LOCALITY. Santa Barbara, California.
PACIFIC COAST DISTRIBUTION. British Columbia to Baja California.

Isolated individuals, including dredged specimens, have been collected from a wide variety of localities. Some are as tall as 22 cm., and correspond to the species as known from the vicinity of Friday Harbor, Washington. Others, fully mature and reproductive, are as small as *F. laciniata* f. *pygmaea* Setchell from San Pedro and other southern localities, and still others fall within the size range of *F. media*, whose type locality is Pacific Grove. There being little to distinguish these from each other except for size, we concur with Doty (1947) and Sparling (1957) in merging all of them under the earliest name, *F. laciniata*. The chief characteristic distinguishing this species from *F. fryeana* and *F. galapagensis* is the occurrence of cystocarps on both the faces and margins of the blades. The majority of the cystocarps have coronate pericarps. An examination of the type specimens of *F. laciniata* and *F. media* in the Agardh and Kylin herbaria, respectively, also showed that a large number (but not all) of the pericarps are so ornamented.

This is a highly variable species in size, shape, color, and general texture, some specimens showing spines and others completely smooth. An evaluation of these characters shows intergrading series. The ecological data we have gathered indicate some correlation between the degree of exposure, the substratum, and depth, with respect to the size and shape of the specimens.

Fryeella Kylin, 1931 NA294

Thalli flat, blade-like, dichotomously branched, the tips blunt and smooth or broadly dissected and irregular. Structurally composed of small flattened cavities separated by arching diaphragms, which may be seen externally with the unaided eye. Cortex of 3–4 layers, with larger inner cells and small outer cells. From the large cells short rhizoids are produced, which contribute partly to the structure of the diaphragms and partly to the thallus walls. Secretory cells abundant on cells of the rhizoids, rarely on the larger cortical cells. Cystocarps scattered over the surface of the thallus, protruding prominently on one side (the lower side on thalli that are repent). Tetrasporangia cruciately divided, in small irregular sori which may become confluent with adjacent sori over the thallus surface.

STRUCTURE AND REPRODUCTION. Kylin, 1931, pp. 15–17.

With one species in the local flora.

NA294
FIG. 41

Fryeella gardneri (Setchell) Kylin

Kylin, 1931, p. 16, figs. 5–6. Doty, 1947A, p. 186.
Fauchea gardneri Setchell, 1901, p. 125. Setchell and Gardner, 1903, p. 313.

Thalli up to 16 cm. tall, repent in thick clusters, or erect as isolated individuals, of a deep rose-red to orange-red color, with a strong blue cast to the lower surface when fresh. Branching of three or four orders, the second and third dichotomies producing the widest segments of the thalli, up to 4 cm. in width, the ultimate segments up to 1 cm. in width, with blunt tips. Cystocarps usually slightly more than 1 mm. in diameter. Tetrasporangia in irregular, grapheiform sori over most of the thallus, or all but the basal 1–2 cm., produced on only one side (the lower surface if repent).

LOCAL DISTRIBUTION. At depths of 20 to 150 feet, at Pescadero Point; Arrowhead Point; Carmel Submarine Canyon; south of Carmel Highlands; Granite Canyon. Dredged from depths of 8–12 fathoms, on sandy mud and growing on worm tubes, on shale at south end of Monterey Bay. Also commonly cast ashore at Moss Beach; Carmel Beach; and near the mouth of Little Sur River.

TYPE LOCALITY. Whidbey Island, Washington.

PACIFIC COAST DISTRIBUTION. Washington; Oregon (Coos Bay); the Monterey region; and at 100 feet off Papalote Bay, Baja California.

NA294

Maripelta Dawson, 1963

Thallus symmetrically peltate from a simple (or branched) cylindrical stipe; blades simple, rotate, expanding from the apex of the stipe and periodically deciduous from each successive, sympodially produced increment; blades showing a medulla of large cells, merging abruptly into a cortex of 2–3 layers of much smaller cells; cystocarps scattered, prominently projecting, ostiolate, located on the upper side of the blade only; tetrasporangia cruciate, in continuous, superficial, pustular nemathecia occupying about ¼

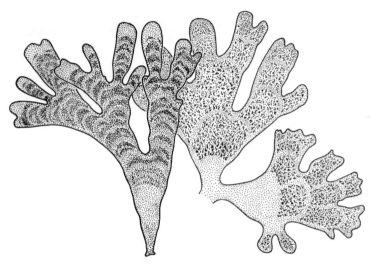

Fig. 41.—*Fryeella gardneri*. Habit of tetrasporangial thallus, left, and of cystocarpic plant, right, showing the nature of fertile areas and the diaphragms characteristic of the genus. ×⅗

of the blade surface along the margin; spermatangia superficial, in pale irregular patches.

STRUCTURE AND REPRODUCTION. Dawson, 1963, pp. 446–49.

With one species in the local flora.

Maripelta rotata (Dawson) Dawson

NA294
Fig. 42

Dawson, 1963, p. 446; pl. 5, fig. 4; pl. 9, figs. 3–4.
Drouetia rotata Dawson, 1949, p. 9; figs. 19–20.

Thallus consisting of a stipe up to 5 cm. tall, terminating in a peltate blade 3–12 cm. in diameter, deep rose-red in color, with a strong blue cast. Blades crisp, the large cells of the medulla easily seen with the unaided eye.

LOCAL DISTRIBUTION. From depths of 50 to 130 feet in the Carmel Submarine Canyon.

TYPE LOCALITY. At 210 to 220 feet, one mile east of White Cove, Santa Catalina Island, California.

PACIFIC COAST DISTRIBUTION. Discontinuously from central California (Monterey region) to Baja California (Punta Eugenio).

Differing from *Constantinea simplex*, which it resembles in habit, by the crisp blades and by the fact that only one blade occurs at a time. In our area, the production of blades appears to be strictly seasonal.

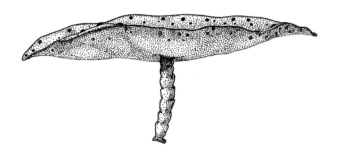

Fig. 42.—*Maripelta rotata.* Habit of thallus, showing peltate blade
bearing cystocarps. ×1½

Rhodymenia Greville, 1830

R299

REVISED KEY TO THE SPECIES IN THE LOCAL FLORA

1. Holdfast a simple disc or cone..................................... 2
1. Holdfast discoid, augmented by stolons........................... 3
  2. Thalli in closely rounded tufts up to
      15 cm. tall........................*R. callophyllidoides* (below)
  2. Thalli not tufted, blades soft and slippery, more
      than 15 cm. tall...................*R. palmata* var. *mollis* (p. 301)
3. Thalli in erect fan-shaped clusters, tips of branches
    broad to spatulate......................*R. pacifica* (p. 301 ; below)
3. Thalli in loose clumps... 4
  4. Blades divided from a short stipe, with acute
      tips............................*R. californica* (p. 300; below)
  4. Blades divided from a long stipe, with blunt tips....*R. lobata* (p. 299)

NC300, 301   **Rhodymenia californica** Kylin var. **attenuata** (Dawson) Dawson

Dawson, 1963, p. 459. (For *R. californica* Kylin, see Smith, p. 300.)
Rhodymenia attenuata Dawson, 1941, p. 139; pl. 19, figs. 10–11; pl. 24, fig. 35.
Smith, 1944, p. 300; pl. 74, fig. 1.

NC299, 301   **Rhodymenia pacifica** Kylin

Kylin, 1931, p. 21; pl. 9, fig. 21. Smith, 1944, p. 301; pl. 76, fig. 1 (including
synonymy).
Rhodymenia lobulifera Dawson, 1941, p. 137; pl. 25, fig. 36. Smith, 1944,
p. 299; pl. 74, fig. 4.

NA298   **Rhodymenia callophyllidoides** Hollenberg and Abbott
FIG. 43

Hollenberg and Abbott, 1965, p. 1184; pl. 1, fig. 4.
Rhodymenia pacifica of Sparling (not of Kylin). Sparling, 1957, p. 359;
pl. 51*b*, figs. 12*a*, *b*, *g*, *j*.

Thallus closely tufted, without apparent stipe or rhizomatous
base, stiff, cartilaginous, orange-brown when fresh and also when

dry. Thalli 8–15 cm. tall, irregularly dichotomously branched to the fifth order, 1.5 cm. wide through the broadest branches, divaricately branched at the tips. Tips somewhat acute or blunt to rounded. Cystocarps projecting from the margins, or on the faces of the upper branches, little modified, or slightly rostrate. A fusion cell is present. Tetrasporangia in mottled nemathecia, submarginal and spreading to the center of the branches. Thallus slightly modified in nemathecial areas.

LOCAL DISTRIBUTION. Dredged from a depth of 10 fathoms, on shale at south end of Monterey Bay; from depths of 8–10 fathoms at various places near the Municipal Wharf and the Coast Guard breakwater in Monterey Harbor. Also found cast ashore at the south end of Carmel Beach.

TYPE LOCALITY. Dredged from a depth of 10 fathoms, on shale at south end of Monterey Bay.

PACIFIC COAST DISTRIBUTION. As above.

Differing from other species of *Rhodymenia* in the local flora by the branching pattern, the more lax nature of the thallus and the orange color. Our recent collections of *R. pacifica* from the inter-

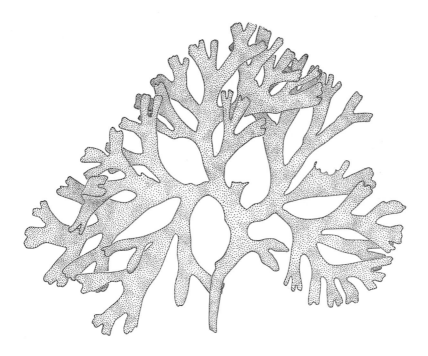

FIG. 43.—*Rhodymenia callophyllidoides.* Habit of thallus, showing repeated branching characteristic of the species. ×½

tidal zone and from 10 fathoms show plants from both habitats to be remarkably similar.

NA294

Rhodymeniocolax Setchell, 1923

Thalli small, pulvinate, up to 0.5 cm. in diameter, parasitically growing on the margins of the older portions of the host, species of *Rhodymenia.* Basal portions solid, penetrating the host.

STRUCTURE AND REPRODUCTION. Sparling, 1957, pp. 362–63.

With one species in the local flora.

NA294 **Rhodymeniocolax botryoidea** Setchell

Setchell, 1923, p. 394. Sparling, 1957, p. 362; fig. 13d–f.

Thalli parasitic, about 3 mm. broad, branches up to 0.75 mm. tall, of a whitish color. Cystocarps terminal. Tetrasporangia cruciate, scattered over the thallus.

LOCAL DISTRIBUTION. Cast ashore on *Rhodymenia pacifica* at Pebble Beach.

TYPE LOCALITY. White's Point, San Pedro, California.

PACIFIC COAST DISTRIBUTION. Lopez Island, Washington; Monterey Peninsula; San Pedro, California; and La Jolla, California.

305

Order CERAMIALES

305

Family CERAMIACEAE

Callithamnion Lyngbye, 1819

R317

REVISED KEY TO THE SPECIES IN THE LOCAL FLORA

1. Thallus with erect branchlets densely intertwined; branches hanging like ropes...................*C. pikeanum* (p. 318)
1. Thallus with erect branches free, branches not rope-like............ 2
    2. With a deeply penetrating basal portion...................... 3
    2. Without a penetrating basal portion.......................... 4
3. Axis conspicuous and percurrent..............*C. biseriatum* (p. 319)
3. Axis inconspicuous, obscurely percurrent.........*C. lejolisea* (below)
    4. Thallus wholly uncorticated, branchlet tips pointed...............................*C. californicum* (p. 318)
    4. Thallus incompletely corticated at base; branchlets with rounded tips.......................*C. rupicolum* (p. 319)

NA317 **Callithamnion lejolisea** Farlow

Farlow, 1877, p. 254. Dawson, 1962, p. 30; pl. 8, figs. 1–2. Smith, 1944, p. 183; pl. 40, figs. 5–7 (excluding synonymy, as *Rhodochorton amphiroae*).

Thalli up to 1 mm. high, forming tufts between the intergenicula of articulated corallines (*Bossiella* and *Calliarthron*), dark red in color. Plants thickly tufted external to the host, with short, little-branched, erect filaments 20–30 µ in diameter. Penetrating rhizoidal portions also tufted, tangled, and nearly colorless. Tetrasporangia terminal on short, 1–3-celled branchlets in lower parts of plant, ovoid, about 35 µ long; cystocarps terminal on short branchlets near base of plant; spermatangia forming terminal, elongate, capitate clusters on short branchlets.

LOCAL DISTRIBUTION. Point Aulon; Point Pinos.
TYPE LOCALITY. San Diego, California.
PACIFIC COAST DISTRIBUTION. Monterey Peninsula; southern California; and Isla San Benito, Baja California.

The original plants on which Smith based his identification of *Rhodochorton amphiroae* have been found in his herbarium, and we agree with Dawson (1962) that Smith misidentified this species and that both the description and the figures refer to *Callithamnion lejolisea*. Nonetheless, *Acrochaetium (Rhodochorton) amphiroae* (Drew) Papenfuss is present in the local flora. NI183

Pleonosporium vancouverianum (J. G. Agardh) J. G. Agardh NC321

J. G. Agardh, 1892, p. 37. Kylin, 1925, p. 57; figs. 37A–C. Smith, 1944, p. 321; pl. 82, figs. 1–2.
Callithamnion vancouverianum J. G. Agardh, 1876, p. 30.
Pleonosporium abysicola Gardner, 1927b, p. 380; pl. 81, fig. 1; pl. 82. Scagel, 1957, p. 208.

Specimens we might have attributed to *P. abysicola* Gardner are somewhat smaller than *P. vancouverianum,* and the spermatangial clusters are sessile rather than on 1–2-celled pedicels. However, after studying many specimens from this area and comparing them with those from the region of the type locality (Friday Harbor) of both of these species, we have concluded that these differences are minor, and that the two species should be merged as *P. vancouverianum.*

Ptilota C. A. Agardh, 1817 NI331

Kylin (1956) removed three western species of *Ptilota* to a new genus, *Neoptilota,* as *N. californica, N. densa,* and *N. hypnoides,* leaving only *P. filicina* in *Ptilota.* These transfers were accepted by Dawson (1961, 1962). We question the transfers.

Neoptilota was separated from *Ptilota* on the basis of the formation of the determinate branches and their occasional transformation into indeterminate branches. Furthermore, the gonimoblasts are said to be produced from indeterminate branches and only exceptionally from determinate branches in the new genus. If our interpretation of these processes is correct, all species on this coast show these characters, in the course of their development. Therefore, pending further evaluation of these characters, we shall continue to use the name *Ptilota* for the four western species.

It should be pointed out that whatever genus name is used, the four species may be separated from each other by the nature of the leaflets. Erroneously, Smith (1944, p. 332; pl. 85, figs. 1–2) attributed a smooth leaflet to *P. californica*. An examination of fragments of the type specimen from Trinity College, Dublin, shows very fine dentations along the abaxial margin of *P. californica* in most of the leaflets. As understood by us, only *P. hypnoides* has entire margins, *P. californica* has slightly dentate to smooth margins, *P. filicina* has serrations on the abaxial, or the abaxial and adaxial surfaces, and *P. densa* on the abaxial only, except on fertile branches, which may have a few teeth on the adaxial as well.

Family DELESSERIACEAE

R334   REVISED KEY TO THE GENERA IN THE LOCAL FLORA

1. Carpogonial filaments and cystocarps restricted to midrib of thallus.... 2
1. Carpogonial filaments and cystocarps scattered over entire blade...... 5
1. Reproductive structures confined to papillae........*Holmesia* (below)
   2. New blades developing from margins of old blades............... 4
   2. New blades developing from midrib of old blades............... 3
3. Branches blade-like, with strong midrib...........*Delesseria* (p. 338)
3. Branches polysiphonous, with no midrib........*Platysiphonia* (below)
   4. Primary and secondary filaments from axial filament
      extending to thallus margin............*Branchioglossum* (p. 335)
   4. Only primary filaments from axial filaments extending
      to thallus margin.....................*Membranoptera* (p. 336)
5. Gonimoblast filaments with carposporangia in chains.............. 6
5. Gonimoblast filaments with carposporangia terminal 12
   6. Thalli free-living... 7
   6. Thalli parasitic...........................*Polycoryne* (p. 347)
7. Tetrasporangial sori scattered over entire blade................. 8
7. Tetrasporangial sori otherwise 10
   8. Blades with a percurrent midrib and opposite
      veins ....*Phycodrys* (p. 342)
   8. Blades without a percurrent midrib.......................... 9
9. Blades with a network of coarse veins.............*Polyneura* (p. 340)
9. Blades with no microscopic veins.............*Myriogramme* (p. 345)
   10. Sori restricted to tips of blades, margins of blades
      frequently toothed ....*Nienburgia* (p. 344)
   10. Sori central or marginal; margins of blades not toothed........ 11
11. Tetrasporangial sori small, oval, and central to branch..*Sorella* (below)

Holmesia J. G. Agardh, 1890

NA334

Thalli erect, flattened, blade-like, with a primary midrib only in the lower portions, and lacking lateral veins. Thallus polystromatic. Reproductive structures on small fertile leaflets produced in the upper half of the blades and giving that portion of the thallus a rough, papillate texture. Young cystocarps with stretched cells between the upper and lower parts of the cystocarpic wall; older cystocarps with a large fusion cell. Carpospores terminal. Tetrasporangia tetrahedrally divided.

STRUCTURE AND REPRODUCTION. Wagner, 1954, pp. 301–3; figs. 74–80. With one species in the local flora.

Holmesia californica (Dawson) Dawson

NA334
FIG. 44

Dawson, 1945, p. 96. Dawson, 1962, p. 80; pl. 35, figs. 6–7; pl. 36. *Loranthophycus californica* Dawson, 1944*A*, p. 655; figs. 1–2.

Thalli erect, membranous, and blade-like, up to 15 cm. tall, rose-colored to deep purple. Attached to rocks by a thin, adherent crust and a few short stolons, giving rise to a tapering stipe of up to 2 cm. in length, expanding into blades 4–7 cm. wide. Blades simple, or irregularly lobed, the margins ruffled or undulate. Cortex of 1–2 layers; medulla of irregularly shaped, colorless cells in 2 layers. Tetrasporangia borne at the distal portions of simple or once-branched erect proliferations at right angles to the thallus. Cysto-carps borne singly on erect, simple, rounded or pointed prolifera-tions, the cystocarps 1 mm. in diameter, with an ostiole. Young cystocarps with stretched cells, the older cystocarps distinguished by a large fusion cell.

LOCAL DISTRIBUTION. Subtidally at 30 to 60 feet, off Cypress Point.

TYPE LOCALITY. Dredged from a depth of approximately 12 fathoms off Point Loma, San Diego, California.

PACIFIC COAST DISTRIBUTION. Subtidally, at Monterey Peninsula; San Simeon; off Santa Cruz Island; Point Loma; and at 80 feet off Punta Santo Tomas, Baja California.

We have examined the specimen reported from Friday Harbor, Washington, and have concluded that it is not of this species.

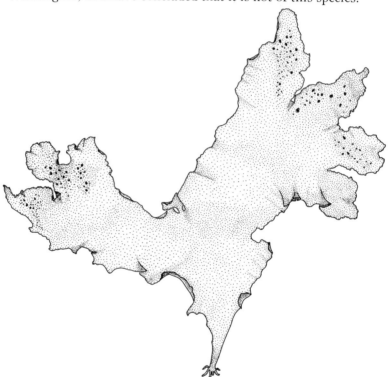

FIG. 44.—*Holmesia californica*. Habit of thallus, showing fertile papillae. ×1

Platysiphonia Börgesen, 1931

Thallus arising from a prostrate basal part attached by rhizoids or from a branched holdfast, variable in size. Branches compressed when young, becoming more or less terete when corticated. Lateral branches endogenous from the central cells. Four pericentral cells; lateral pericentral cells each forming 2 flanking cells that do not divide further. Thallus varying from ecorticate in some species to heavily corticate in others. Cystocarps and stichidia not, or only slightly, corticated near the base.

STRUCTURE AND REPRODUCTION. Womersley and Shepley, 1959, pp. 168–223; pl. 5.

With one species in the local flora.

Platysiphonia clevelandii (Farlow) Papenfuss NC,R371

Papenfuss, 1944, p. 206.
Taenioma clevelandii Farlow, 1877, p. 236. Smith, 1944, p. 370; pl. 96, figs. 4–5.

Thalli epiphytic, or on rocks covered with sand, up to 3 cm. tall, brownish-red in color, slippery to touch. Prostrate portion with rhizoids usually 2 cells long, and with the basal portion of the rhizoid considerably modified into a lobed or digitate disc. Erect shoots freely branched, but with 6 or more segments between successive branches. Cystocarps borne low on the branches, up to 0.5 mm. in diameter. Tetrasporangia produced in ultimate blades, in two longitudinal rows.

LOCAL DISTRIBUTION. Cast ashore at Moss Beach; Fanshell Beach; south end of Carmel Beach. Young plants have been found epiphytic on corallines; older ones on *Nereocystis* holdfast.

TYPE LOCALITY. San Diego, California.

PACIFIC COAST DISTRIBUTION. Discontinuous, from central California (Pigeon Point, San Mateo County) to Baja California (Scammon Lagoon).

Sorella Hollenberg, 1943 NC,R340

Differing from *Erythroglossum* in the relatively narrow thallus divisions and the distribution of tetrasporangial sori, usually small and oval and occurring singly in the center of the branches, whereas in *Erythroglossum* they are numerous and scattered near the margins of the relatively wide thallus divisions.

STRUCTURE AND REPRODUCTION. Hollenberg, 1943, pp. 577–78; figs. 13–16.

With one species in the local flora.

Sorella divaricata (Setchell and Gardner) Hollenberg NC340

Hollenberg, 1943, p. 578.
Erythroglossum divaricatum Setchell and Gardner *in* Gardner, 1926, p. 207; pl. 17, fig. 2. Smith, 1944, p. 340; pl. 87, fig. 7.

No new collections of this rare alga have been made, so it is not possible to assess whether this species might be merged with *S. delicatula* var. *californica,* as has been suggested by Hollenberg.

NA334

Nitophyllum Greville, 1830

Thalli erect, 5–25 cm. tall, blade-like, undivided, or in various ways lobed or divided, upper portions one cell thick, lower portions more than one cell thick with cells regularly cut off from one another. Midrib, nerves, and microscopic veins lacking. Growing point with a marginal meristem and without a transversely dividing apical cell. Cystocarps distributed on the surface of the thallus, as are the tetrasporangial and spermatangial sori. Carpospores terminal.

STRUCTURE AND REPRODUCTION. Kylin, 1924, p. 69.

With one species in the local flora.

NA334
FIG. 45

Nitophyllum northii Hollenberg and Abbott

Hollenberg and Abbott, 1965, p. 1185; pl. 2, fig. 6.

Thalli up to 14 cm. tall, up to 6 cm. broad, cuneate, shortly stipitate, membranous, and blade-like, upper portions broadly furcate, or more commonly dissected, and sometimes proliferous. Color orange-red, drying to a soft pink. The color of plants from 100 feet is lighter than those from 30 feet. Cystocarps with terminal spores; spermatangial sori lunate to ovoid, 2 mm. long by 1–2 mm. wide; tetrasporangial sori elliptical, 1 or 2 tetrasporangia appearing in a cross section of a sorus.

LOCAL DISTRIBUTION. Subtidally, from 30 to 100 feet, in the Carmel Submarine Canyon, epiphytic on a variety of algae. Also cast ashore at the south end of Moss Beach, and on Carmel Beach.

TYPE LOCALITY. At 100 feet in the Carmel Submarine Canyon, growing on *Prionitis.*

PACIFIC COAST DISTRIBUTION. As above, and at a depth of 30 feet, off Imperial Beach, San Diego County.

Resembling *Hymenena setchellii* in appearance, but lacking the ruffled margin characteristic of that species, and lacking microscopic veins. Also resembling *Myriogramme spectabilis,* which also lacks microscopic veins, but having terminal carpospores instead of carpospores in chains. It is difficult to separate these two species if cystocarpic plants are not available.

NA334

Acrosorium Zanardini *in* Kützing, 1869

Thalli epiphytic or saxicolous, mostly small, blade-like, flattened, irregularly branched, one cell thick throughout most of its

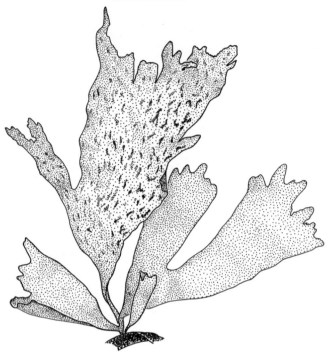

FIG. 45.—*Nitophyllum northii.* Habit of fertile thallus taken from the Carmel Submarine Canyon. ×1

length; only the lower portions 3–5 cells thick. Macroscopic veins lacking, microscopic veins present. With a marginal meristem, and lacking an apical cell dividing transversely. Cystocarps distributed over the thallus, the carpospores terminal. Tetrasporangia in a single massive sorus near the tips of the end segments.

STRUCTURE AND REPRODUCTION. Papenfuss, 1939, pp. 11–20; figs. 1–30.

With one species in the local flora.

Acrosorium uncinatum (Turner) Kylin

NA334
FIG. 46

Kylin, 1924, p. 78; Dawson, 1962, p. 94; pl. 43, fig. 2.
Fucus laceratus var. *uncinatus* Turner, 1808, p. 153; pl. 68, figs. *c–d.*

Thalli epiphytic or saxicolous, up to 8 cm. tall, deep rose-red in color. Erect portion of narrow blades up to 2 cm. wide, but usually less, the blades toothed irregularly and occasionally with hooks. Thalli growing on stones appear to be more robustly developed than the epiphytic thalli. No reproduction seen in local plants.

LOCAL DISTRIBUTION. Dredged from depth of 8–10 fathoms, on shale at south end of Monterey Bay; and at similar depths near the Municipal Wharf, Monterey.

TYPE LOCALITY. England.

PACIFIC COAST DISTRIBUTION. Monterey Peninsula; and from southern California to Baja California (Bahia Santa Maria).

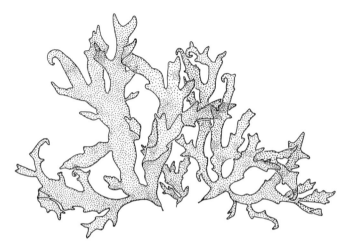

FIG. 46.—*Acrosorium uncinatum*. Habit of thallus growing on rock, showing hooked terminal portions of some branches. ×1

R354
FIG. 47

Botryoglossum farlowianum (J. G. Agardh) De Toni var. **farlowianum** Hollenberg and Abbott

Hollenberg and Abbott, 1965, p. 1185, fig. 13.

With tetrasporangial sori in lateral proliferations only.

LOCAL DISTRIBUTION. Common at all rocky headlands, and as listed in Smith.

TYPE LOCALITY. Monterey, California.

PACIFIC COAST DISTRIBUTION. From British Columbia (Vancouver Island) to Baja California (Punta San Quintin).

R354
FIG. 48

Botryoglossum farlowianum (J. G. Agardh) De Toni var. **anomalum** Hollenberg and Abbott

Hollenberg and Abbott, 1965, p. 1186, fig. 12.

With tetrasporangia in linear sori at the tips of the branches, and in lateral proliferations.

LOCAL DISTRIBUTION. Mussel Point; Point Pinos; Middle Reef of Moss Beach; south end of Carmel Beach.

TYPE LOCALITY. Mussel Point.

PACIFIC COAST DISTRIBUTION. Duxbury Reef, Marin County, to Pismo Beach, San Luis Obispo County.

The placement of tetrasporangial sori in lines along the upper and marginal terminal veins, as well as in lateral proliferations, raises the question of whether this variety might not more properly belong in *Hymenena,* close to *H. flabelligera,* which has tetrasporangia in such linear sori. We have so far been unable to settle this question satisfactorily, and at this point can state only that perhaps half of the plants collected in this area show this anomalous position of tetrasporangia.

This variety is not as common as var. *farlowianum.*

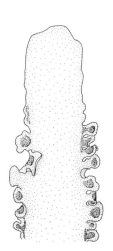 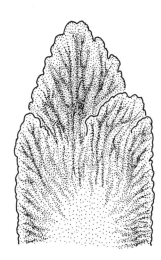

FIG. 47 *(left)—Botryoglossum farlowianum* var. *farlowianum.* Habit of thallus, showing characteristic pattern of sori. ×4

FIG. 48 *(right)—Botryoglossum farlowianum* var. *anomalum.* Habit of thallus, showing characteristic pattern of sori. ×4

Botryoglossum ruprechtiana (J. G. Agardh) De Toni

NA353
FIG. 49

De Toni, 1900, p. 676.
Nitophyllum ruprechtiana J. G. Agardh, 1872, p. 51.
Cryptopleura ruprechtiana (J. G. Agardh) Kylin, 1924, p. 93. Doty, 1947, p. 195.
Nitophyllum stenoglossum J. G. Agardh, 1898, p. 92.
Cryptopleura stenoglossum (J. G. Agardh) Kylin, 1924, p. 92.
Nitophyllum marginatum J. G. Agardh, 1898, p. 93.
Cryptopleura spatulata Gardner, 1927, p. 241; pl. 27. Dawson, 1962, p. 100; pl. 48, fig. 2.

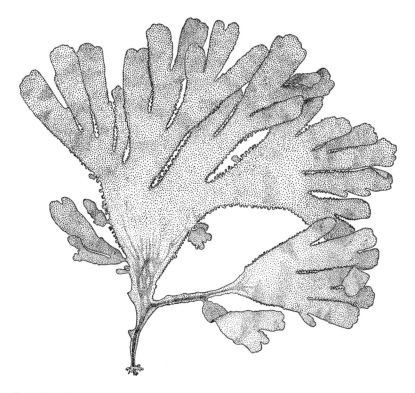

Fig. 49.—*Botryoglossum ruprechtiana*. Habit of thallus, showing discrete proliferations along upper portions of branches. ×½

Thalli saxicolous, up to 30 cm. tall, brick-red to orange-red. Basal portion of mature erect branches rarely stem-like, or eroded, but if stipitate, 1–5 cm. long, the upper portions winged from erosion. Macroscopic veins marked only on main axis, lacking in flabellae. Flabellae arising from a foliar stipe, or directly from the basal portions, branching 4–5 times in a regular to irregular dichotomous manner, the segments of the second and third order up to 3 cm. in width, the upper segments more narrow, the tips broad, spathulate, blunt or irregularly notched. Texture delicate. Margins smooth; or the margins of the main segments with proliferations less than 1 mm. long, and the margins on the upper (but never the terminal) segments discrete, 1–2 mm. wide. Cystocarps mostly in the larger proliferations but sometimes submarginal. Tetrasporangia in discrete sori in proliferations only.

LOCAL DISTRIBUTION. Dredged from depths of 6–10 fathoms in Monterey Harbor, on shale or a sandy, muddy bottom; subtidally from 40 to 90 feet in the Carmel Submarine Canyon. Also cast ashore east of Mussel Point and east of Point Pinos.

TYPE LOCALITY. "Northwest coast of North America."

PACIFIC COAST DISTRIBUTION. Puget Sound; Oregon; Monterey region; Santa Barbara, California; La Jolla, California; and Islas Todos Santos, Pacific Mexico.

Differing principally from *B. farlowianum* in the delicate texture of the blades and in having discrete proliferations, instead of the densely ruffled margin caused by numerous proliferations as in *B. farlowianum.*

Family DASYACEAE

KEY TO THE GENERA IN THE LOCAL FLORA   R356

1. Main axis flattened, branching distichous, branches
   in a dense fringe.........................*Rhodoptilum* (below)
1. Main axis cylindrical, branches alternate and distichous,
   not fringing the axis.....................*Heterosiphonia* (below)

Rhodoptilum Kylin, 1956   R356

Differing from *Dasyopsis* in the large number of monosiphonous, branched, "pseudoaste" (false branches) arising from the thallus margins. These branches are lacking in *Dasyopsis.*

With one species in the local flora.

Rhodoptilum densum (Smith) Dawson   NC356

Dawson, 1961, p. 448.
Dasyopsis densa Smith *in* Smith and Hollenberg, 1943, p. 217. Smith, 1944, p. 356; pl. 92, fig. 2.

LOCAL DISTRIBUTION (additional). Subtidally, at depths of 40 to 90 feet, in the Carmel Submarine Canyon. Also cast ashore near the mouth of Little Sur River.

We strongly suspect that when enough specimens of this species and the northern species, *R. plumosum,* are compared, *R. densum* may be merged with *R. plumosum.* The differences that we can now evaluate seem very small and perhaps of a degree not warranting continued recognition of two species. However, more material is necessary for a further comparison before the evidence may be said to be conclusive.

Heterosiphonia Montagne, 1842   NA356

Thalli erect, distichously alternate, branches at intervals of 2–3 (or more) segments, the pseudolaterals usually polysiphonous at the base but the ultimate ramuli usually monosiphonous. Main axes if corticated, the cortication not extending to the tip; where the polysiphonous condition is evident; pericentral cells mostly not transversely divided. Tetrasporangia and spermatangia in stichidia. Cystocarps sessile, solitary on the base of lateral branches.

STRUCTURE AND REPRODUCTION. Kylin, 1956, p. 461.

With one species in the local flora.

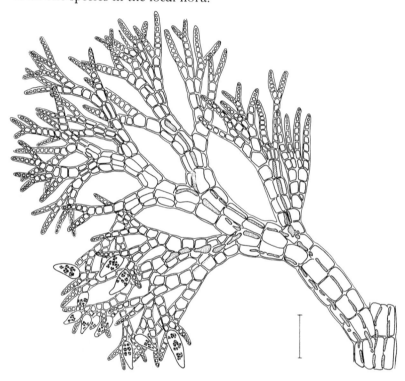

FIG. 50.—*Heterosiphonia asymmetria.* Habit of thallus, showing tetrasporangial stichidia. (Rule represents 100μ.)

NA356
FIG. 50

Heterosiphonia asymmetria Hollenberg

Hollenberg, 1945, p. 449; figs. 7–9. Dawson, 1963*A*, p. 402.

Thalli erect from a small disc, 2–12 cm. tall, of a deep rose-red color. Main axes cylindrical near the base, compressed above, the segments scarcely longer than wide; five pericentral cells, never transversely divided, of unequal size and arranged constantly with two opposite the other three. Branching alternate in a distichous manner on both the main and lateral branches, the sympodial arrangement clear microscopically. Branches of the first order bearing no small branchlets and therefore appearing naked, those of the second order perhaps naked at their bases. Branchlets of the third order up to 2 cm. long. All branches except the ultimate polysiphonous, the stichidia borne with, and appearing to replace, branches of the ultimate orders. Tetrasporangia in pairs on a flattened cylinder, the stichidium frequently with an acute apex.

LOCAL DISTRIBUTION. Dredged from depths of 6–10 fathoms, on worm tubes and on the back of a *Cryptochiton,* on shale at south end of Monterey Bay. Also cast ashore at the south end of Carmel Beach.

TYPE LOCALITY. Intertidal on rocks near Corona del Mar, California.

PACIFIC COAST DISTRIBUTION. Monterey region. Also dredged from a depth of 34–35 fathoms, at White Cove, Santa Catalina Island. Intertidally at Corona del Mar, California.

Only tetrasporangial plants have been found locally.

Family RHODOMELACEAE

REVISED KEY TO THE GENERA IN THE LOCAL FLORA   R357

1. Thalli free-living 2
1. Thalli parasitic 12
  2. Thallus branches not compacted in a flat sheet................. 3
  2. Thallus branches laterally compacted into a
     flat sheet.............................*Amplisiphonia* (p. 372)
3. With ultimate branches uncorticated........................... 4
3. With all branches completely corticated......................... 9
  4. Erect branches radially branched in a spiral succession........... 5
  4. Erect branches alternately and distichously branched........... 7
5. Thalli with a prominent creeping, prostrate system
   of branches...............................*Lophosiphonia* (p. 364)
5. Thalli essentially erect; creeping portion, if any, inconspicuous...... 6
  6. Thalli with colored monosiphonous laterals........*Veloroa* (below)
  6. Thalli with colorless monosiphonous laterals
    (trichoblasts)....................*Polysiphonia* (p. 358; below)
7. With three simple branches between two successive
   compound branches.......................*Herposiphonia* (p. 368)
7. Without simple branches regularly between successive compound
   branches... 8
  8. Erect branches with a percurrent axis. .*Pterosiphonia* (p. 365; below)
  8. Erect branches without a percurrent axis.....*Pterochondria* (p. 367)
9. Branches with a small pit at apex...........*Laurencia* (p. 376; below)
9. Branches without a pit at apex............................... 10
  10. Branches cylindrical 11
  10. Branches flattened ....*Odonthalia* (p. 375)
11. Spermatangial stichidia discoid.................*Chondria* (p. 372)
11. Spermatangial stichidia not discoid.............*Rhodomela* (p. 374)

12. Thallus pyriform, terminal on branches
   of host ....*Erythrocystis* (below)
12. Thallus cushion-like, lateral on branches
   of host ....*Janczewskia* (p. 381)

NA357

Veloroa Dawson, 1944

Thalli small, monopodial with a sparingly branched monosiphonous main axis and large, persistent, monosiphonous, colored, lateral branches. Polysiphonous main axis with four pericentral cells, ecorticate. Tetrasporangia borne in a spiral row of 8–15, one per segment.

STRUCTURE AND REPRODUCTION. Dawson, 1944, p. 335; pl. 72, fig. 2. Dawson, 1963, p. 414, pl. 133.

With one species in the local flora.

NA357 **Veloroa subulata** Dawson

Dawson, 1944, p. 335; pl. 72, fig. 2.

Plants, as found on the Monterey Peninsula, up to 2 cm. tall, attached by slender tufts of rhizoids, with four ecorticate pericentral cells and composed of segments 1–2 diameters long, bearing colored monosiphonous tapering laterals, which arise one per segment in ¼-spiral sequence and which may be one to four times forked. Tetrasporangia one per segment in spiral sequence in the branches. Sexual plants unknown.

LOCAL DISTRIBUTION. Collected from a depth of 10 fathoms off Mussel Point, Pacific Grove; and from about 2 fathoms on a sardine hopper, near Mussel Point.

TYPE LOCALITY. Growing on hydroids at a depth of 70 feet, Tepoca Bay, Gulf of California, Mexico.

PACIFIC COAST DISTRIBUTION. As above.

Since the tetrasporangia are not in special stichidia it seems best to recognize *Veloroa* as a genus close to but distinct from *Brongniartella.*

Polysiphonia Greville, 1824

R359   REVISED KEY TO THE SPECIES IN THE LOCAL FLORA

1. Segments with four pericentral cells............................. 2
1. Segments with more than four pericentral cells.................... 4
   2. Trichoblasts and scar-cells lacking or very rare...*P. pacifica* (p. 359)
   2. A trichoblast, scar-cell, or a branch on every segment............ 3
3. Each branch replacing a trichoblast.............*P. acuminata* (p. 360)
3. Each branch axillary to a
   trichoblast...................*P. flaccidissima* var. *smithii* (p. 361)

4. Major branches completely corticated..........*P. brodiaei* (p. 361)
4. All branches uncorticated.................................. 5
5. Trichoblast or scar-cell on every segment not bearing a branch;
    each a quarter-turn to right of one below.......*P. paniculata* (below)
5. Trichoblasts or scar-cells not present on every segment
    without a branch......................*P. hendryi* (p. 363; below)

Polysiphonia paniculata Montagne   NC362

Montagne, 1842, p. 254. Howe, 1914, p. 142. Hollenberg, 1944, p. 480, fig. 7.
Polysiphonia californica Harvey, 1853, p. 48. Anderson, 1891, p. 224. Kylin, 1941, p. 36. Smith, 1944, p. 362; pl. 93, fig. 1.
Polysiphonia senticulosa Anderson, 1891, p. 224. (Not of Harvey.)

Polysiphonia hendryi var. gardneri (Kylin) Hollenberg   NC363

Hollenberg, 1961, p. 355; pl. 4, fig. 1; pl. 5, fig. 3.
Polysiphonia collinsii Hollenberg, 1944, p. 481, figs. 2, 8. Smith, 1944, p. 363.
Polysiphonia sancti-petri Collins, *in* Phyc. Bor.-Amer. No. 2247 (name only).

Pterosiphonia Falkenberg, 1897

REVISED KEY TO THE SPECIES IN THE LOCAL FLORA   R365

1. Older branches completely corticated..............*P. baileyi* (p. 367)
1. All branches uncorticated....................................... 2
  2. Branches cylindrical ....*P. bipinnata* (p. 366)
  2. Branches compressed 3
3. Branches markedly flattened, two segments between successive
    branches of erect filaments...................*P. dendroidea* (p. 366)
3. Branches moderately flattened, mostly three segments between
    successive branches of erect filaments............*P. gracilis* (below)

Pterosiphonia gracilis Kylin   NA365
                                              FIG. 51

Kylin, 1925, p. 72; fig. 47a.

Plants, as found on the Monterey Peninsula, up to 3 cm. high, distichously and laxly branched to several orders of branching. Branches and determinate branchlets cylindrical or slightly compressed, ecorticate. Laterals, arising at intervals of 2–3 segments, with attachment involving only one segment. Main branches 200–250 µ in diameter, with segments 0.5–0.7 diameters long. Ten to 14 pericentral cells. Determinate laterals tapering to acute tips.

LOCAL DISTRIBUTION. On piling, Municipal Wharf, Monterey; dredged from a depth of 10 fathoms, on shale at south end of Monterey Bay; and from low littoral near Malpaso Creek.

TYPE LOCALITY. San Juan County, Washington.

PACIFIC COAST DISTRIBUTION. Southern British Columbia to Central California (Monterey).

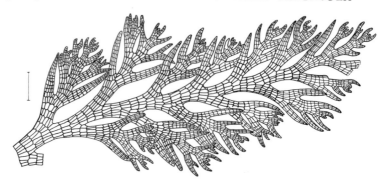

Fig. 51.—*Pterosiphonia gracilis.* Habit of thallus, showing compressed nature and the mostly three-segment separation of successive branches. (Rule represents 200μ.)

NC369 ## Herposiphonia parva Hollenberg

Hollenberg, 1943, p. 575.

Smith, 1944, p. 369; pl. 96, fig. 2 (as *H. pygmaea* Hollenberg, a superfluous name).

LOCAL DISTRIBUTION (additional). On worm tubes, dredged in Monterey harbor at 8–10 fathoms; and at −0.6 feet, Pescadero Point.

TYPE LOCALITY. Growing on corallines above low-tide level near Lady's Harbor, Santa Cruz Island, California.

PACIFIC COAST DISTRIBUTION. Oregon; Monterey; Santa Cruz Island.

Laurencia Lamouroux, 1813

R377 REVISED KEY TO THE SPECIES IN THE LOCAL FLORA

1. Thalli with the erect branches laterally adjoined in a
 cushion-like mass....................................*L. crispa* (p. 378)
1. Thalli with erect branches free from one another...................2
 2. Branches markedly compressed................................3
 2. Branches approximately cylindrical...........................5
3. Thallus loosely tufted, more than 10 cm. tall.......................4
3. Thallus densely tufted, less than 8 cm. tall..........*L. blinksii* (below)
 4. Main axis more than 3 mm. wide, lower
  axis naked..............................*L. spectabilis* (p. 377)
 4. Main axis less than 2 mm. wide, lower axis with
  many branches..........................*L. splendens* (p. 377)
5. Thallus a spreading clump, tips of some branches with
 tendril-like attachments....................*L. subopposita* (below)
5. Thallus a compact clump, branches without tendrils.................6
 6. Erect portions loosely branched, usually nodding
  in one direction..........................*L. gardneri* (p.379)
 6. Erect portions profusely branched in stiff
  radial whorls...............................*L. pacifica* (p. 378)

Laurencia blinksii Hollenberg and Abbott

NA377
Fig. 52

Hollenberg and Abbott, 1965, p. 1186; pl. 2, fig. 5.

Plants saxicolous, crisp, in erect, dense tufts 4–7(9) cm. high and nearly as wide. Erect branches complanate and basically alternately distichous, the distichous branching often obscured by divergent growth and crowding of the branches. Subultimate branches lanceolate to conical in outline. Fruiting branches irregularly lobed or divided. Medulla of large cells without lenticular thickenings, surface cells 25–44 μ long by 13–15 μ wide in surface view, slightly radially elongate in cross section.

LOCAL DISTRIBUTION. On rocky shore south of the mouth of Carmel River; and on exposed rocky shores near Malpaso Creek.

TYPE LOCALITY. Just south of Malpaso Creek.

PACIFIC COAST DISTRIBUTION. As above.

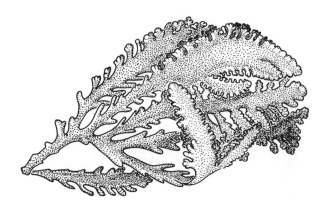

FIG. 52.—*Laurencia blinksii.* Habit of thallus, showing clustering characteristic of the species. ×1½

Laurencia subopposita (J. G. Agardh) Setchell

NA377
Fig. 53

Setchell, 1914, p. 9.
Chondriopsis subopposita, J. G. Agardh, 1892, p. 149.

Plants epiphytic on various algae, irregularly and sparingly to densely branched, with branches of several orders of varying length and with frequent terminal hooks that develop secure tendril-like attachments to the host and to other branches of the epiphyte, resulting locally in tangled masses to 30 cm. across and 25 cm. high. Cortical cells more or less isodiametric, not palisade-like. Medullary cells without lenticular thickenings. Tetrasporangia ovoid,

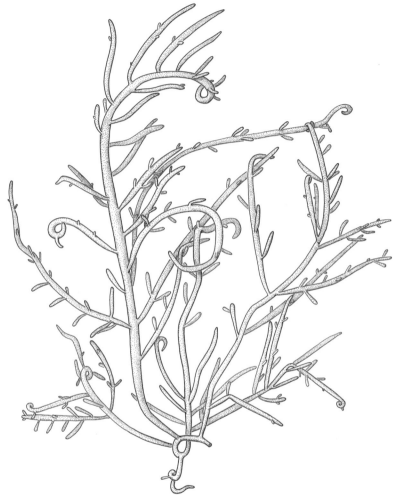

Fig. 53.—*Laurencia subopposita*. Habit of portion of thallus, showing
tendrils characteristic of the species. ×1

60–80 μ in diameter, on terminal parts of short laterals 1–2 mm.
long and about 500 μ in diameter. Sexual plants unknown.

LOCAL DISTRIBUTION. Cast ashore at Pebble Beach, epiphytic on corallines and *Gastroclonium*. At —1.0-foot tide level, on *Gastroclonium*, at
Pebble Beach.

TYPE LOCALITY. Santa Barbara, California.

PACIFIC COAST DISTRIBUTION. Central California (Pebble Beach) to
Pacific Mexico (Punta San Eugenio).

Erythrocystis saccata (J. G. Agardh) Silva NC380

Silva, 1952, p. 308.
Ricardia saccata (J. G. Agardh) Kylin, 1928, p. 94, figs. 59–64. Smith, 1944, p. 380; pl. 98, fig. 2.
Chylocladia saccata J. G. Agardh, 1849, p. 89.
Erythrocystis grevillei J. G. Agardh, 1876, p. 639.
Ricardia montagnei Farlow (not of Derbès and Solier). Farlow, 1877, p. 237. Anderson, 1891, p. 223. Phyc. Bor.-Amer. No. 338.
Ricardia montagnei var. *gigantea* Farlow, *in* Algae Exsicc. Amer. Bor. No. 58. Farlow, 1889, p. 2. Setchell, 1905, p. 60.

BIBLIOGRAPHY FOR SUPPLEMENT

Many references cited in the *Supplement* already appear in the Bibliography to the Smith; none of these are listed below.

ABBOTT, ISABELLA A. **1961.** On Schimmelmannia from California and Japan. *Pacific Naturalist,* 2(7) : 379–86. 2 pls.

——. **1962.** Structure and reproduction of Farlowia (Rhodophyceae). *Phycologia,* 2(1) : 29–37. 12 figs.

ABBOTT, ISABELLA A., AND R. E. NORRIS. **1965.** Studies on Callophyllis (Rhodophyceae) from the Pacific Coast of North America. *Nova Hedwigia,* 10(1/2) : 67–84. pls. 6–19.

AGARDH, J. G. **1842.** *Algae maris mediterranei et adriatici* . . . Paris. x + 164 pages.

——. **1890.** Till Algernas Systematik (Afd. 4). *Lunds Univ. Årsskr.,* Ser. 2. Avd. 2, 1(3). 125 pp. 3 pls.

——. **1894A.** *Analecta algologica. Continuatio I.* Lund. 144 pp. pls. 1–2. *Lunds Univ. Årsskr.,* 29 (Afd. 2, Nr. 9) : 1–144. pls. 1–2.

ARDRÉ, FRANCOISE, AND PAULETTE GAYRAL. **1961.** Quelques Grateloupia de l'Atlantique et du Pacifique. *Revue Algologique,* 6(1) : 38–48. pls. 2–4.

ARESCHOUG, J. E. **1881.** Beskrifning pa ett nytt algslägte Pelagophycus, hörande till Laminarieernas familj. *Bot. Notiser,* 2 : 49–50.

BATTERS, E. A. L. **1892A.** On Conchocelis, a new genus of perforating algae. *Phycol. Mem.,* 1 : 25.

BLACKLER, HELEN. **1963.** Some observations on the genus Colpomenia. *Proc. 4th Internat. Seaweed Symposium.* Oxford: Pergamon. pp. 50–54.

BRAVO, LENORE K. **1962.** A contribution to knowledge of the life history of Prasiola meridionalis. *Phycologia,* 2(1) : 17–23. 4 figs.

——. **1965.** Studies on the life history of Prasiola meridionalis. *Ibid.,* 4(3) : 177–94. 27 figs.

CHIHARA, M. **1965.** Germination of the carpospores of Bonnemaisonia nootkana, with special reference to the life cycle. *Phycologia,* 5(1) : 71–79.

DAWSON, E. Y. **1944.** The marine algae of the Gulf of California. *Allan Hancock Pacific Expeditions,* 3(10) : 189–453.

——. **1944A.** A new parasitic red alga from Southern California. *Bull. Torrey Bot. Club,* 71 : 655–57. figs. 1–4.

——. **1945.** Notes on Pacific Coast marine algae, III. *Madroño,* 8(3) : 93–97. 1 pl.

——. **1949.** Studies of Northeast Pacific Gracilariaceae. *Allan Hancock Foundation Publ. Occ. Pap.,* No. 7 : 1–105. pls. 1–25.

——. **1949A.** Contributions toward a marine flora of the southern California Channel Islands, I–III. *Allan Hancock Foundation Publ. Occ. Pap.,* No. 8 : 1–57. pls. 1–15.

——. **1950.** Notes on some Pacific Mexican Dictyotaceae. *Bull. Torrey Bot. Club,* 77(2) : 83–93.

——. **1950A.** On the status of the brown alga, Dictyota Binghamiae J. G. Agardh. *Wasmann Jour. Biol.,* 8(3) : 267–69.

——. **1953.** Marine red algae of Pacific Mexico, Part I. Bangiales to Corallinaceae Subf. Corallinoideae. *Allan Hancock Pacific Expeditions,* 17(1) : 1–239. pls. 1–33.

———. 1954. Marine red algae of Pacific Mexico, Part II. Cryptonemiales (cont.). *Allan Hancock Pacific Expeditions,* 17(2) : 241–397. pls. 1–44.

———. 1961. A guide to the literature and distributions of Pacific benthic algae from Alaska to the Galapagos Islands. *Pacific Science,* 15(3) : 370–461.

———. 1961A. Marine red algae of Pacific Mexico, Part IV. Gigartinales. *Pacific Naturalist,* 2(5) : 191–341. pls. 1–61.

———. 1962. Marine red algae of Pacific Mexico, Part VII. Ceramiales: Ceramiaceae, Delesseriaceae. *Allan Hancock Pacific Expeditions,* 26(1) : 1–207. pls. 1–50.

———. 1963. Marine red algae of Pacific Mexico, Part VI. Rhodymeniales. *Nova Hedwigia,* 5 : 437–76. pls. 77–95.

———. 1963A. Marine red algae of Pacific Mexico, Part VIII. Ceramiales: Dasyaceae, Rhodomelaceae. *Nova Hedwigia,* 6 : 401–81. pls. 126–71.

———. 1964. A review of Yendo's jointed coralline algae of Port Renfrew, Vancouver Island. *Nova Hedwigia,* 7 : 537–43.

DAWSON, E. Y., AND R. L. STEELE. 1964. An Eastern Pacific member of Yamadaia (Corallinaceae) from the San Juan Islands, Washington. *Nova Hedwigia,* 8 : 1–4. pls. 1–2.

DAWSON, E. Y., C. ACLETO, AND NINJA FOLDVIK. 1964. The seaweeds of Peru. *Nova Hedwigia Beihefte*: 1–111. pls. 1–81.

DE LA PYLAIE, A. 1829. Flora de Terre-Neuve et des iles Saint Pierre et Miquelon. Paris. 128 pp.

DERBÈS, A., AND A. J. J. SOLIER. 1850. Sur les organes reproducteurs des algues. *Ann. Sci. Nat., Sèr. 3, Bot.,* 14 : 261–82.

DE TONI, J. B. 1900. *Sylloge algarum,* 4(2) : 387–776.

DIXON, P. S. 1964. Taxonomic and nomenclatural notes on the Florideae, IV. *Bot. Notiser,* 117 : 56–78.

DIXON, P. S., AND G. RUSSELL. 1964. Miscellaneous notes on algal taxonomy and nomenclature, I. *Bot. Notiser,* 117 : 279–84.

DOTY, M. S. 1947. The marine algae of Oregon, Part I. Chlorophyta and Phaeophyta. *Farlowia,* 3(1) : 1–65.

———. 1947A. The marine algae of Oregon, Part II. Rhodophyta. *Farlowia,* 3(2) : 159–215. pls. 11–14.

DREW, KATHLEEN. 1956. Reproduction in the Bangiophycidae. *Bot. Rev.,* 22 : 553–611.

FAN, K. C. 1959. Studies on the life histories of marine algae I. Codiolum petrocelidis and Spongomorpha coalita. *Bull. Torrey Bot. Club* 86 : 1–12. figs. 1–40.

FARLOW, W. G., C. L. ANDERSON, AND D. C. EATON. 1877–89. Boston. *Algae Exsiccatae Bor.-Amer.,* Fasc. 1–5.

FELDMANN, J. 1954. Inventaire de la flore marine de Roscoff. Supp. 6. *Trav. de la station biologique de Roscoff.* 152 pp.

FRIEDMANN, I. 1959. Structure, life-history, and sex determination of Prasiola stipitata Suhr. *Ann. Bot.* n.s. 23 : 571–94.

GARDNER, N. L. 1940. New species of Melanophyceae from the Pacific Coast of North America. *Univ. Calif. Publ. Bot.,* 19 : 267–86. pls. 30–35.

HAMEL, G. 1931–39. Phéophycées de France. *Traite de botanique.,* 47. 432 pp.

HOLLENBERG, G. J. 1939A. Culture studies of marine algae. I. Eisenia Arborea. *Am. Jour. Bot.,* 26 : 34–41.

———. 1943. New marine algae from Southern California. II. *Amer. Jour. Bot.,* 30 : 571–79.

———. 1944. An account of the species of Polysiphonia on the Pacific Coast of North America. II. Polysiphonia. *Amer. Jour. Bot.,* 31(8) : 474–83.

———. 1945. New marine algae from Southern California. III. *Amer. Jour. Bot.,* 32(8) : 447–51. figs. 1–9.

——. **1958.** Observations concerning the life cycle of Spongomorpha coalita (Ruprecht) Collins. *Madroño,* **14**(8) : 249–51. figs. 1–7.

——. **1958A.** Culture studies of marine algae. III. Porphyra perforata. *Am. Jour. Bot.,* **45** : 653–56. figs. 1–15.

——. **1959.** Smithora, an interesting new algal genus in the Erythropeltidaceae. *Pacific Naturalist,* **1**(8) : 3–11.

——. **1961.** Marine red algae of Pacific Mexico, Part V. The genus Polysiphonia. *Pacific Naturalist,* **2**(5–6) : 345–75.

HOLLENBERG, G. J., AND ISABELLA A. ABBOTT. **1965.** New species and new combinations of marine algae from the region of Monterey, California. *Canadian Jour. Bot.,* **43** : 1177–88. 2 pls. 13 figs.

KÜTZING, F. T. **1869.** *Tabulae phycologicae.* Nordhausen. Vol. 19: iv + 36 pp. 100 pls.

KYLIN, H. **1947.** Über die Fortpflanzungsverhaltnisse in der Ordnung Ulvales. *Förhandl. Kgl. Fysiografiska Sallsk. i Lund,* **17**(19) : 1–9.

——. **1956.** *Die Gattungen der Rhodophyceen.* Lund : CWK Gleerups. xv + 673 pp.

LEVRING, T. **1955.** Contributions to the marine algae of New Zealand. I. Rhodophyta : Goniotrichales, Bangiales, Nemalionales and Bonnemaisoniales. *Arkiv for Botanik.* Öfvers. *Kgl. Svensk. Vetensk. Ak. Förh.,* Ser. 2, **3**(11) : 407–32. 15 figs.

——. **1960.** Contributions to the marine algal flora of Chile. *Lunds Univ. Årsskr.* N.F. (Avd. 2). **56**(10) : 1–83.

MASON, LUCILLE R. **1953.** The crustaceous coralline algae of the Pacific Coast of the United States, Canada, and Alaska. *Univ. Calif. Publ. Bot.,* **26**(4) : 313–90. pls. 27–46.

MATHIESON, A. C. **1965.** Contributions to the life history and ecology of the marine brown alga Phaeostrophion irregulare S. et G. on the Pacific Coast of North America. (Thesis, University of British Columbia, Vancouver.) 113 pp. 15 tables. 92 figs.

MONTAGNE, J. F. C. **1839.** Plantes cellulaires. *Algae,* **7** : 1–110. Paris.

——. **1842.** Plantes cellulaires exotiques. *Ann. Sci. Nat. Bot., Ser. 2,* **18** : 241–82.

——. **1842A.** *Prodomus generum specierumque phycearum novarum, in itinere ad polum antarcticum* . . . Paris. 16 pp.

——. **1846.** Phyceae. *In* C. GAUDICHAUD, *Voyage autour du monde exécuté pendant les années 1836 et 1837 sur sa corvette* La Bonite . . . Paris. pp. 1–112.

NÄGELI, C. **1861.** Beiträge zur Morphologie und Systematik der Ceramiaceae. *Sitzungsber. k. b. Akad. Wiss.* Munschen., **2** : 297–415.

NORRIS, R. E. **1957.** Morphological studies on the Kallymeniaceae. *Univ. Calif. Publ. Bot.,* **28** : 251–334. pls. 28–40. 25 text figs.

OKAMURA, K. **1909.** *Icones of Japanese algae.* Tokyo. **1** : 1–258. pls. 1–40. (Published by the author.)

PAPENFUSS, G. F. **1939.** The development of the reproductive organs in Acrosorium acrospermum. *Bot. Notiser,* **1939** : 11–20. figs. 1–30.

——. **1944.** Structure and taxonomy of Taenioma, including a discussion on the phylogeny of the Ceramiales. *Madroño,* **7** : 193–214. pls. 23–24.

——. **1945.** Review of the Acrochaetium-Rhodochorton complex of the red algae. *Univ. Calif. Publ. Bot.,* **18** : 299–334.

——. **1947.** Further contributions toward an understanding of the Acrochaetium-Rhodochorton complex of the red algae. *Univ. Calif. Publ. Bot.,* **18** : 433–47.

——. **1950.** Review of the genera of algae described by Stackhouse. *Hydrobiologia,* **2** : 181–208.

——. **1958.** Notes on algal nomenclature. IV. *Taxon,* **7**(4) : 104–9.

PARKER, B. C., AND E. Y. DAWSON. **1964.** Notes on variability and range in the elk kelp Pelagophycus. *Trans. San Diego Soc. Nat. Hist.,* **13** : 301–8. 2 figs.

POWELL, H. T. **1957.** Studies in the genus Fucus L. I. Fucus distichus L. emend. Powell. *Marine Biol. Assoc. U.K. Jour.,* **36** : 407–32. pls. 1–2.

——. **1957A.** Studies in the genus Fucus L. II. Distribution and ecology of forms of Fucus distichus L. emend. Powell in Britain and Ireland. *Ibid.,* **36** : 663–93. pls. 1–4.

ROSENVINGE, L. K. **1900.** Note sur une Floridée aérienne (Rhodochorton islandicum nov. sp.). *Bot. Tidsskr.,* **23** : 61–81.

SCAGEL, R. F. **1957.** An annotated list of the marine algae of British Columbia and Northern Washington. *Natl. Mus. Canada Bull.,* **150.** vi + 289 pp.

SCHMITZ, C. J. F. **1889.** Systematische übersicht der bisher bekannten Gattungen der Florideen. *Flora,* **72** : 435–56. pl. 21.

SEGAWA, S. **1955.** Systematic anatomy of the articulated corallines. (Supplementary report.) The structure and reproduction of Yamadaia melobesioides Segawa. *Bot. Mag. Tokyo,* **68**(807) : 241–47.

SETCHELL, W. A., AND N. L. GARDNER. **1930.** Marine algae of the Revillagigedo Islands Expedition in 1925. *Proc. Calif. Acad. Sci.,* **19**(11) : 109–215.

SILVA, P. C. **1952.** A review of nomenclatural conservation in the algae from the point of view of the type method. *Univ. Calif. Publ. Bot.,* **25** : 241–324.

——. **1953.** The identity of certain Fuci of Esper. *Wasmann Jour. Biol.,* **11**(2) : 221–32.

——. **1957.** Notes on Pacific marine algae. *Madroño,* **14**(2) : 41–51.

SMITH, G. M. **1944.** *Marine algae of the Monterey Peninsula, California.* Stanford: Stanford University Press. vii + 622 pp. 98 pls.

SPARLING, SHIRLEY R. **1957.** The structure and reproduction of some members of the Rhodymeniaceae. *Univ. Calif. Publ. Bot.,* **29**: 319–96. 15 figs. pls. 48–59.

SVEDELIUS, N. **1956.** Are the haplobiontic Florideae to be considered reduced types? *Bot. Tidsskr.,* **50** : 1–24.

TAYLOR, W. R. **1945.** Pacific marine algae of the Allan Hancock Expeditions to the Galapagos Islands. *Allan Hancock Pacific Expeditions,* **12** (I–IV) : 1–528. 100 pls.

THURET, G. **1854A.** Note sur la synonymie des Ulva lactuca et latissima L. suivie de quelques remarques sur la tribu des Ulvacées. *Mém. Soc. Imp. Sci. Nat. de Cherbourg,* **2** : 17–32.

VICKERS, ANNA. **1905.** Liste des algues marines de la Barbade. *Ann. Sci. Nat. Bot., Ser. 9.* **1** : 45–66.

WAGNER, FLORENCE S. **1954.** Contributions to the morphology of the Delesseriaceae. *Univ. Calif. Publ. Bot.,* **27** : 279–346. 290 text figs.

WITHERING, W. **1792.** *An arrangement of British plants;* . . . Ed. 2., **4.** Birmingham. 412 pp.

WITTROCK, V. B. **1866.** Försök till en monographi öfver algslägtet Monostroma. (Thesis, Stockholm.) 66 pp. 4 pls.

WOMERSLEY, H. B. S., AND E. A. SHEPLEY. **1959.** Studies on the Sarcomenia group of the Rhodophyta. *Austral. Jour. Bot.,* **7** : 168–223. pls. 1–5.

YAMADA, Y. **1948.** *In* YAMADA, Y., AND S. KINOSHITA. *Icones of the marine animals and plants of Hokkaido. Marine Algae, No. 1*: 1–18. pls. 1–22. Hokkaido Fisheries Scientific Institution. Yoichi, Hokkaido.

YENDO, K. **1902.** Corallinae verae of Port Renfrew. *Minn. Bot. Stud.,* **2**(40) : 711–20.

INDEX

New additions to the flora are in **boldface** type; those with an asterisk (*) are recorded from this area for the first time. New taxon names (names recognized in the *Supplement* but not in Smith) are in CAPITAL AND SMALL-CAPITAL letters; those with a double dagger (‡) are published here for the first time. Synonymies are in *italics*; those with a dagger (†) are names that had been recognized by Smith. Other names are in plain roman type, in some cases followed by (NI), new information; (RD), revised description; (RK), revised key; or other, self-explanatory, notations. Index categories are discussed in detail in the Introduction.